The Coral Reef

The Coral Reef

ALAN EMERY

Canadian
Broadcasting
Corporation

PAGE 1: *Alcyonarian soft corals occur in many weirdly shaped forms. They retract their polyps when disturbed.*

TITLE PAGE: *Humbugfish, such as this Indian Ocean species, feed on plankton but never move more than about a metre from a particular thicket of coral during their entire adult lives. If threatened, they dive for cover amongst the branches of their coral "home."*

PICTURE ACKNOWLEDGEMENTS
Ruby Cler: pages 53, 99, 107
Alan Emery: pages 1, 2-3, 7, 9, 11, 14, 18, 26, 30, 31, 39, 43, 46, 48, 50, 51, 54, 55, 56, 58, 63, 70, 72, 74, 76, 79, 80, 82, 86, 92, 94, 102
David Hunt: Front jacket, pages 15, 23, 27, 34, 36, 38, 59, 69, 77, 87, 88, 93, 105
Courtesy of the *Royal Ontario Museum*, Toronto, Canada: page 45
Kaf Smith: pages 16, 28, 33, 47, 62, 67, 71, 75, 83, 91

CREDITS
The CBC television program *The Coral Reef* was produced as part of the series *The Nature of Things* by the following people: Executive Producer: *James Murray*; Producer, Director and Writer: *John Bassett*; Consultant: *Dr. Alan Emery*, Royal Ontario Museum; Cinematography: *Neville Ottey, John Stoneman*; Underwater Lighting Technician and Camera Assistant: *Ruby Cler*; Editor: *John Gareau*; Music Consultant: *Pat Russell*; Production Assistants: *Kay Nagao, Lars Isaksson*; Acknowledgement to: *Bellairs Research Institute of McGill University*, St. James, Barbados.

Text © Alan Emery 1981
Photographs © the photographers
as credited 1981
All rights reserved.

Published by CBC Merchandising
for the
Canadian Broadcasting Corporation.

CBC Merchandising
Canadian Broadcasting Corporation
Box 500, Station A
Toronto, Ontario
M5W 1E6

Design: Keith Abraham
Line drawings: Deborah Drew-Brook
Printed in Canada
5 4 3 2 1 81 82 83 84 85

Canadian Cataloguing in Publication Data

Emery, Alan, 1939-
  The coral reef

Based on the program The coral reef, from the CBC television series The Nature of things.
Includes index.
ISBN 0-88794-093-5

l. Coral reef ecology. I. The Nature of things (Television program).
II. Title.

QH541.5.C7E43   574.5'26367
C81-094229-1

Contents

Introduction

The Coral Garden

Few people can stand by the water's edge and fail to wonder what lies hidden below the restless and tenuous blue veil that hides the undersea world from our eyes. We can look at the sea from the shoreline, and examine what she discards onto the beach, but the ocean depths remain a mystery that has fascinated us for centuries. We have admired the power and beauty of the waves and tried to portray the moods of the water in words and images. This sense of wonder, of innate curiosity about the unknown, has drawn people to roam the ocean's surface.

The first heroic explorers brought back romantic tales and drawings of enormous and dangerous sea monsters, and modern knowledge has discounted only some of these creatures as fanciful. Huge squids, gigantic sharks and fish with mouths big enough to swallow a man whole, all live in the sea. These dangers, combined with the sea's unpredictable nature, have injected an ambivalence into our attitude. We want to enter the sea, to become a part of the encompassing water, but we are afraid, and perhaps a little repelled.

European oceans can be dark, cold and dangerous, but when the early explorers travelled to the tropics, they found emerald lagoons surrounded by idyllic islands. White or rose-hued sand beaches ringed these little aquatic jewels, and the water was clear and inviting. Fish abounded in unfamiliar, luxuriant underwater growth that looked like a submerged forest or garden. But the paradise was not without its dangers. Warm, tranquil waters were prickled with poisonous spines,

OPPOSITE: *On a coral reef the branched and sometimes leaf-like organisms that proliferate in what appears to be an underwater garden are in fact animals, such as corals. Brightly coloured fishes like this red-and-white hawkfish hide in the coral branches.*

dark shadows could dart out of the garden and turn into deadly sharks, delicious fish sometimes caused wracking agonies and death, while at other times the same fish were safe to eat.

Of all the unknown areas of the ocean, the coral reef was the most attractive and at the same time the most repellant. It was beautiful, but dangerous; bountiful, but deadly; close, yet inaccessible. The native peoples had a deep respect for the coral reef and its inhabitants because they had become part of the reef, depending on it for food and tools. European explorers also came to live by coral reefs, but it was an uneasy association. The reef gave them food, but wrecked their boats. It provided building materials, but in storms the ocean would claim them back. There was water, but not to drink, unless they could drill to find it in the deep recesses of the coral platform underfoot.

The history of concerted effort to understand coral reefs is surprisingly short. The first person to record his ideas of how reefs form was a remarkably perceptive young scientist by the name of Charles Darwin, whose epic voyage aboard the military vessel *Beagle* in 1832 carried him to many tropical atolls in the open ocean. Darwin's resulting theory of evolution and his insights into coral reef origins were among the forces that inspired the first truly oceanographic expedition in 1872, when an English research vessel, the *Challenger*, began a five-year voyage making the first systematic record of marine plants and animals. Although her main interest was in the deep sea, nevertheless she brought back many species which were new to science, and which were found only on coral reefs.

Cataloguing and classification is the first critical step in describing and understanding any biological system, although it sheds little light on the life histories and inter-relationships of the coral reef creatures. Nearly one hundred years after Darwin's theories on the origins of coral reef atolls were published in 1842, another expedition left England to travel to the Great Barrier Reef of Australia. After two years of study on these isolated islets in 1928-29, Dr. Maurice Yonge and his colleagues wrote a many-volumed work, *The Great Barrier Reef Expedition*, that profusely illustrated the results of their collections, experiments and observations. It took several years to publish all the books, but long before the last one appeared, the scientific world was beginning to appreciate the marvellous intertwining of life histories in a coral reef community. Yonge's books are still the cornerstone of the study of coral reef ecology. In the early 1950s, two geologists, Harry S. Ladd and Joshua I. Tracey of the U.S. Geological Survey, tested Darwin's theory of atoll formation and found it to be correct.

Early stumbling attempts were made to walk through the ocean, pumping air down through a hose from a boat to the diver. In 1942, Jacques-Yves Cousteau's invention of SCUBA diving using simple equipment made possible a whole new vista of understanding. Cousteau's simple "Aqualung" and the concept of free-swimming in the ocean while breathing air carried in tanks on the diver's back has enabled us to travel in the reefs without being impossibly awkward. Now we can enter the once-forbidden realm, now we can see and swim

Skeletons of meandering brain coral (left) and labyrinthine brain coral (right). Individual polyps are not identifiable in brain corals. Instead they have become continuous, often taking meandering shapes.

with an ease that resembles, if it does not duplicate, that of the fishes.

In the early 1930s, a scientist, William H. Longley, who was studying in the Tortugas made the first underwater colour photograph. To get enough light, he built a double canoe with a sling between them full of magnesium powder. He opened the shutter underwater and by a remote trigger, fired the magnesium powder. The resulting flash provided ample light, but rapidly became an explosion which consumed both the sling and the two canoes. It was an expensive photograph.

Longley's efforts heralded innovations in underwater photography that are still being developed at an incredible pace, largely because of the marriage of SCUBA and modern electronic technology. Daring men and women have brought back unparalleled records in vivid colour. The experience has been made popular in motion pictures and television, and this has created an interest in coral reefs that extends far beyond the scientific community.

Although we are still a long way from full understanding, we can now chart the overall mechanisms by which the reef survives. Explorations have shown the reef to be full of puzzles. The animals are often bizarre in shape or gaudy in colour and there are more species on reefs than in any other aquatic location. For most people, even years of diving cannot erase the sense of wonder and amazement that is one's inevitable first impression of being in the water over a coral reef.

Among the scientists who have struggled to probe the mysteries of the reef, two daring individuals stand out. Thomas Goreau, who worked at the University of the West Indies in Jamaica, spent thousands of hours diving to great depths on the nearby reefs. He described the mechanisms of wave erosion resistance that depended on the growth form of the corals. Subjects as diverse as the mineralogy of coral skeletons and the reproduction of sponges came under his scrutiny. Conrad Limbaugh, working in the Pacific Ocean, pioneered research into the habits of the peculiar "cleaner fishes," research that forced a new appreciation of the intricately interwoven dependencies of coral reef species. In the late 1960s each of these men met an untimely and tragic death in the sea, but they left behind them an enthusiasm as well as a definition of needed areas of research.

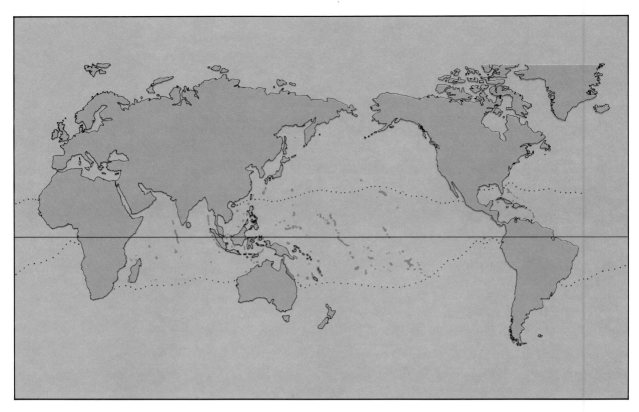

World distribution of coral reef formations.

In 1970, a small group of North American scientists conceived a project to describe the ecology of a coral reef, beginning with one large example—they chose an atoll called Glover's Reef in the Caribbean—and to enlist the aid and expertise of every marine scientist in the world who was capable of working on some aspect of charting the cycles and life histories of a coral reef. Surprisingly few people qualified. Funds were obtained from the U.S. National Science Foundation to plan this enormous undertaking. It was based on a gigantic computer-generated model of the ecology of a coral reef, a model that was derived from the most up-to-date theories. Each of the fifty or sixty scientists was to be assigned an area of the project, eventually combining their efforts in a vast enterprise that would take at least ten years to complete.

Biological sciences have never enjoyed the luxury of vast sums of money, and so while the National Science Foundation, the richest research-granting agency in the world, recognized the value of the proposal, it could not begin to find the $20 million that was called for in the proposal. The dream of understanding coral reefs through one enormous, unified and organized effort was not to be realized—at least not then. Perhaps sometime in the future there will be an opportunity to try again.

In the meantime, scientists devised two less grandiose forums to pursue and spread knowledge about reefs. The first is a series of summary papers on reefs, published under one editorship. The second is a series of international symposiums on coral reefs, a project which began in 1972 and which is growing stronger each year, as scientists present the results of their most current research. In an informal but highly effective way, the study of the coral reef is being organized through co-operation and communication on an international scientific level. Energetic and dedicated men and women are able to debate the latest theories, be exposed to the criticism of their peers, and to build on one another's ideas and knowledge.

Today, the world's store of knowledge about coral reefs is partly to be found in the research papers and books that have been published, but it is largely still either germinating in the minds of students and scientists, or hidden in the sway and surge of the reef waters. Coral reef research is still in a time of controversy, a time of frustration for lack of funds and the hugeness of the perceived areas of ignorance. But it is also a time of drama, when each year we can expect to see more parts of the puzzle fall into place.

It is the purpose of this book to provide a summary of the ecology of coral reefs, in a form that does not require a familiarity with scientific terminology or literature to be understood. There are many paradoxes, and many questions that have been left unanswered. You may find that you are frustrated by wanting to ask a question, but that you are not sure exactly what you want to ask. These are the same feelings and responses that marine scientists have as they try to unravel the mysteries of the coral reef.

This book will not make the final and definitive statement on the ecology of a coral reef. The knowledge simply does not exist for that statement to be made. But there is enough known that we can begin to appreciate and understand the delicate nature of the reef, and its importance to us as human beings. It is our purpose to bring that understanding and appreciation to you.

This carnation coral skeleton demonstrates how growth and reproduction may take place by a process of "budding" in which one polyp divides into two.

Chapter One
Origins of the Reef

The words coral reef define a massive structure composed of coral that is close enough to the surface of the water to change the course of the surface currents and waves. Some reefs are so huge that they resemble underwater mountains, and for this reason they are often thought of as geological structures rather than biological ones. Both are correct interpretations.

Unlike many other types of reefs, the coral reef is the result of the growth of living animals and plants. The most important of these is the coral itself, an animal which builds a stony skeleton.

The reef is a very ancient structure in geological history. Geologists can identify ancient reefs easily because the plants and animals that produced them had stony skeletons, and the shapes that they left behind are well preserved. Tracing the fossil record of reefs back through the hundreds of millions of years of geological time reveals that reef environments have been in existence for at least two billion years, and that those earliest reef builders were among the very first forms of life on the earth. Called stromatolites, these early plants were a type of blue-green algae or seaweed that could build reefs because of their peculiar talent for trapping grains of sand and other debris in their thin filamentous strands. The reefs they formed — unimposing lumps of brown-grey matted sandstone cemented into roundish blobs — bore no resemblance to the modern coral reef. But this was the beginning, and these early reef builders remained unchanged for nearly one and a half billion years, three times as long as the entire known history of animals composed of more than a single cell. Even today there exists a living stromatolite reef in isolated Shark's Bay in Australia.

Approximately six hundred million years ago, reef-building animals invaded the stromatolite reefs. These animals (archaeocyathids) looked like sponges, but had a stony feel. The union of these two living reef builders, one a plant, one an animal, began an association that has never ceased.

After seventy-five million years of successful reef building, for some reason almost every reef community suddenly disappeared, the first of three major disasters in geological history. Eventually, about four hundred million years ago, a successor reef community arose that had renewed vigour. Stromatolites came back accompanied by an advanced kind of plant that could capture and secrete a limestone-like material which made them resistant to the action of the waves. As well as the hard-bodied plants, there emerged limestone-secreting animals, called corals, that grew sheltered in long stony tubes. In one type, there were parallel floors at regular intervals in the tubes (tabulate corals), and in the other, the outer face of the tubes was wrinkled (rugose coral). Many other animals, including a type of sponge (stromatoporoid) which took several shapes from branching to lumpy, and the moss animals (bryozoans), then formed huge flourishing colonies. This multiform community also included other ancient animals that were not reef builders, such as many kinds of predacious fishes.

Gradually, changes in the climate of the world reduced the favourable conditions for tabulate and rugose corals. Although a few corals hung on, they were never in abundance throughout this period of retrenchment. But even without the abundance of corals, the reef was still a rich and successful community.

Suddenly, a mammoth and planet-wide catastrophe struck, when fully half of the world's animals, both terrestrial and aquatic, were wiped out. The tabulate and rugose corals became extinct, the stromatolite community was dealt a near-mortal blow, and the reef community virtually disappeared for the second time. Whatever change took place so long ago, it demanded of the creatures an evolutionary response to meet the new needs. The old corals, the stromatolites, the stromatoporoid sponges and many others could not meet that challenge.

It is still a mystery, and the cause of the disaster is often the subject of heated debate. We do know that previously, the continents had been massed together in a single super-continent called Pangaea. Precisely at the time disaster swept the biological world, the continents began to break up, and the gigantic and globe-encircling Tethys Sea gradually became partitioned into smaller oceans. An east-west split across the middle of the super-continent opened a belt of warm water eventually forming a new ocean basin which became the cradle for a whole new reef community, the one which is familiar to us today. Then the two major remaining land masses began to split from north to south, and the Atlantic Ocean was born. Other splits and

Some corals are found in the deep, cold water of the Norwegian fjords, or in the black depths of the open ocean. But because these deep-water corals never grow into massive formations near the surface of the water, and do not affect the currents or waves of the ocean surface, they are not considered to form reefs.

Most corals have a very thin layer of living tissue, often delicately hued, covering a deceptively sharp limestone skeleton, as in this Pacific branching coral.

drifting continental masses created the Indian Ocean, the Pacific Ocean and the seas dotted with tiny islands, such as the Coral Sea, the Celebes Sea and the Red Sea. With so many isolated oceans and continental islands, evolutionary changes took place at an unprecedented rate, and since then the number of species in existence has almost certainly been multiplied by more than four.

But the reef community and the land were to suffer one more all-encompassing debacle, the third and last. Seventy million years ago, nearly one-third of all animal species were wiped out. This disaster tolled a death knell for dinosaurs on the land, and because of a fifty to sixty per cent reduction in the amount of shallow ocean, the loss of thousands of species of reef animals and plants. From this devastation, modern reefs have arisen, and the earth now houses more species than it has ever seen before.

The most obvious fossil reefs are the islands that surround the lagoons of many tropical atolls. In some cases, the reefs which grew beneath the sea emerged when the earth's crust bent upward, carrying the reef with it. Other islands emerged when the sea level fell during the ice ages. Incredible volumes of sea water were bound up in the glaciers, lowering the sea level as much as hundreds of metres.

This left the corals high and dry, to die in the sun. Significant changes in sea level have occurred as recently as the last 15,000 years.

As the coral weathered and eroded in the air and rain, plants grew on the new islands. During the first centuries, a thin humus or topsoil developed so that trees could grow. When the ice ages retreated, some of these islands drowned in the rising ocean to become the base for new coral reefs. Other islands are still poking out of the water, often only a few metres above the water's surface.

Living coral reefs under the water are found roughly between the geographical boundaries of the Tropics of Capricorn and Cancer, although where a current of warm water or some other special factor keeps the temperature tropical, they may stray further to the north or south. For instance, a warm current of water coming westward across the Atlantic Ocean splits and flows south along the Brazilian coast allowing reef corals to grow as far south as southern Brazil. By contrast, the west coast of South America enjoys the rich, but cold Humboldt Current flowing northward along the coast. The southern limit of reef growth on this coast is almost 1,500 kilometres further north than on the east coast. The most northerly reef corals are found in the warm and tranquil waters of the Red Sea.

Coral is found in the greatest abundance where winter and summer tropical extremes of temperature are nearly the same, and where other climatic and natural conditions also remain nearly unchanged year round. Clear water is also important, and too much silt in the water will smother the living tissue of the corals. Conditions for coral growth are ideal, in terms of temperature, all along the coast of South America from the island of Trinidad eastward to Cape San Roque, the easternmost tip of the continent. Yet, because of the flow of the Amazon and other large rivers along the coast, the sediment in the water makes it impossible for coral reefs to form, although sponge reefs have been found just in front of the Amazon, where fresh water floats on top of the heavier sea water.

Many ancient reefs lie buried under the ground in areas that are now cold, and have been found to be a source of large deposits of oil and natural gas. Since we know that coral reefs are found only in tropical or sub-tropical waters, we can assume that in the distant geological past, the wintery reaches of the northern parts of Asia and Canada must have been at one time washed by the warm waters of a tropical sea filled with luxuriant coral reefs.

At night, the living polyps of the star coral expand their tentacles to catch plankton.

The only other major requirement for reef-building corals to survive seems to be that they need a firm place to settle in shallow water. If you were to colour a map of the world in those places where the water was very clear, very warm and shallow, you would have coloured over most of the world's large, living coral reefs. In the Caribbean, the best-developed reefs are in the Bahamas, along the north shore of Cuba, off the southeastern coast of Central America (where large rivers do not colour the water), and near the windward islands of the Lesser Antilles. The biggest coral reef in the world is the Great Barrier Reef of Australia—thousands of kilometres long and in places as much as one hundred kilometres across—the largest biological structure in the world.

Other large concentrations of corals near continents are found off the eastern African coast, off the eastern Central American coast, and in the Persian Gulf. Magnificent reefs lie nearly untouched in the relatively inaccessible areas of the Indo-Malaysian Archipelago. Surrounding almost all of the tiny islands that dot the tropical Pacific Ocean and the Indian Ocean are corals, or the islands themselves are coral. Tahiti, Fiji, Palau, the Marshall and Marianas islands and the Maldives, conjure up idyllic settings of sand beaches, palm trees and turquoise waters. In some ways, these are perhaps the most spectacular of the reefs for an individual observer, because they are big enough to be opulently rich in life forms, but small enough that they can become familiar.

While each reef has its own unique characteristics, some common features are used to classify the reefs into three major types: atoll, fringing and barrier reefs. These classifications refer to the location of the reef and the length of time it has been growing. Essentially, atolls are island reefs, and barrier reefs are continental. Fringing reefs are the beginning stages of both types.

How do coral reefs grow into the different forms? Darwin proposed a theory on atoll formation which was published nearly 150 years ago. Since then, modern studies have expanded his theory, so that now we can explain more fully how atolls are formed.

Think of a brand-new mountain, the result of a newly erupted and cooled volcano, which juts, bare and lofty, through the ocean's surface. It is black, barren basaltic rock without a trace of life on it. The ocean waters, which were thrown hissing back from the mountain's hot rising shoulders, now wash gently against the shores. Waves splash against it, but there are no beaches.

Upstream from the island there will be old coral reefs surrounding islands that were born thousands of years before. In these reefs, there is a constant production of young of all of the species that occur there. Nearly ninety per cent of the young begin this free-living existence in a tiny larval stage, that enables them to travel away from their birthplace by hitching a ride on the ocean currents that are drifting by. Many of the larvae are grotesque or bizarre. Often they are studded with long bristles or spines, which make them sink more slowly through the currents, creating the same effect as a parachute has in air. Others have little paddles, or small water pumps that act as mini jet engines. Once out in the ocean currents, the larvae feed and grow quickly. Some stay out for only a short while; others, like the spiny lobster, may drift for as long as six months or more.

When the larvae reach a large enough size, they begin to search for a suitable place to settle, and swim actively towards the ocean bottom. If the bottom is too deep, many die or are eaten before they can settle, and some of these larval animals find the barren rock inhospitable. But the coral larvae settle quickly onto clean surfaces. If the water is shallow and clear, and if there is a current passing by to carry food to them as settled adults, the larvae will change into young corals in an amazingly short period of time. This metamorphosis, which can involve a complete alteration in shape and colour, may happen in a few hours.

After a period of time, the larvae of many corals and other creatures will have settled around the new volcanic island on the underwater rocks to a depth of no more than a few hundred metres. As soon as the metamorphosis is completed, the juvenile coral begins to grow quickly. The coral animal or polyp will lay down a skeleton of calcium carbonate, which is cemented to the rock of the mountain. Unlike our internal human skeleton, this one, shaped like a small, circular cup, is laid down around the outside of the animal. As the polyps grow, they secrete a new floor and then new walls to the cup. Each of the new floors is cemented onto the floor beneath it, with the result that the polyp rises continually higher off the original rocky bottom on a growing pedestal of calcium carbonate.

Corals are also capable of a type of reproduction that does not require the larval stage. A bulge in the side of one of the adults near the base of the colony suddenly appears, and begins to enlarge. As it gets bigger, it takes on the shape of an adult polyp. This new individual also secretes a limestone cup onto the mountain. In this way the burgeoning coral colony expands in width. Many of these buds are produced when there is a place for them to set down the limestone cup. When the whole base is big enough (perhaps a few centimetres across) to support the branches, the colony of individuals, which may have

ABOVE: *Elkhorn, or plate coral, is a fast-growing, shallow-water species that has relatively large polyps, and is characteristic of the wavy, reef-top areas of fringing reefs.*

RIGHT: *Plants are the only organisms that directly trap the energy of the sun. On coral reefs it is unusual to see long filamentous strands of algae such as this Pacific species, because herbivores usually keep it grazed to a very short length.*

started from a single larva, begins to grow upward in earnest. Each coral species has a unique shape, the result of different patterns of budding and growth. If for some reason the coral dies, and the surface is left bare, then this surface is itself an attractive place for other coral larvae to settle and begin anew.

Most new mountains in the sea are the result of volcanoes, and they tend to be shaped like inverted cones. The level at which the first coral larvae were laid down would have been an underwater ring around the mountain, the diameter of which is fixed by the diameter of the mountain at the maximum depth the coral larvae settled. With time, the corals grow upward covering the mountain's underwater shoulders until they brush the surface waves. At this stage of development, the reef is said to be "fringing" because it forms a complete circle around the mountain, out to where the waves break over the outer edge of the ring of coral. The growth is rarely so complete as to cut off the island completely. Breaks or passes can usually be found, and it was through these that early explorers ran their small boats onto the beaches.

It is a curious fact that new mountains are really floating. They are not floating in the water, but are floating on the earth's inner crust. This layer of the earth behaves something like the asphalt on a road in the hot summer sun, as a heavy object sitting on asphalt slowly sinks into it. The mountain is an extremely heavy object sitting on a layer of "rock" that acts like slow-motion asphalt. Over hundreds of thousands of years, the mountain which once drove its spire high into the air will gradually sink beneath the waves.

As the mountain sinks, it drags the coral down with it. But the manner in which the coral grows allows it to keep up with the sinking mountain, and to maintain a living layer of coral animals in shallow water. This living layer, however, is being maintained on an ever-increasing thickness of old floors, which were made of calcium carbonate or limestone. The limestone ring increases in thickness, and its seaward face, growing more rapidly than the rest becomes a vertical wall, as the whole ring rises upward like a chimney, being built by millions of little coral polyps madly piling new floors on the old ones and cementing them down in an effort to keep up with the sinking mountain.

The sinking mountain settles deeper beneath the surface, until the tip of the volcanic cone nestles under the water and there is no land above the water between one side of the chimney of coral and the other. Many processes of reef erosion create a sandy debris, which gradually covers the last traces of the mountain, leaving a deep bowl of calcareous sand in the centre. This deep bowl is the jewel-like lagoon of an atoll.

Although Darwin did not have any idea why the mountain might sink, and although he could not even see that there was a mountain under the reef, he guessed that it had to be there. Thus, he could explain why all atolls have a circular, or nearly circular shape, and why there was a bowl of shallow water in the middle. He could also suggest a reason for the sheer vertical cliffs that extended a thousand metres

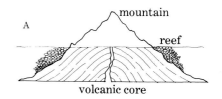

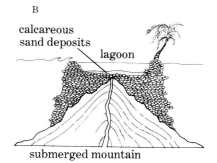

A fringing reef (A) forming around the shores of a new volcanic mountain gradually becomes an atoll formation (B) as the mountain slowly sinks back into the sea.

Fringing reefs (A) *along continental coasts gradually become barrier reefs* (C) *as the elkhorn and staghorn thickets merge with the developing buttress and groove formation* (B) *to form a shallow area between them where a coralline algal ridge develops and gradually marches offshore.*

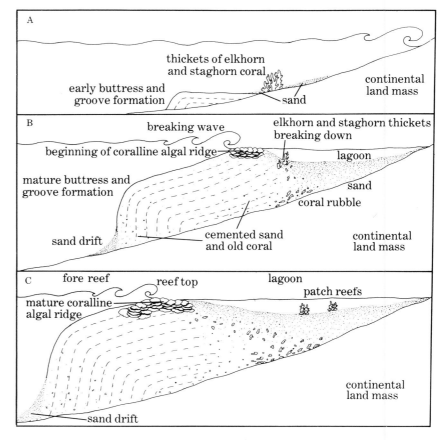

underwater straight down from the breakers surrounding an atoll. He did not enjoy the complete agreement of other scientists, but then, Darwin's theories on many subjects were not universally popular. Over one hundred years later, geologists drilled down thousands of metres through a coral reef lagoon. Finally they hit the mountain top, and found that it was, precisely as Darwin had predicted, the top of a volcano.

Many tropical parts of continents are also bordered by reefs. Some are snugly fitted to the shoreline and can be seen as fringing. Others do not fringe the shoreline, but seem to form protective barriers that are often many kilometres offshore. The barrier reef off the Florida Keys is on an average eight kilometres offshore. Turneffe Reef off the Central American coast is fifty to one hundred kilometres offshore, and the trip to the Great Barrier Reef off Australia's coast is in the order of one hundred and fifty kilometres.

As we have seen, six hundred million years ago, an association began between animals and algae in reef communities. Although the types of algae have changed dramatically, the role of the limestone-trapping or limestone-secreting algae has since then been a critical factor in the formation of reefs. These encrusting algae are found on the outside front of reefs, facing the open ocean where the waves break, where they enjoy the most brilliant sunlight in the shallowest

Years ago	Event
2,000,000,000	Reefs begin.
600,000,000	Reefs are invaded by animals called archaeocyathids.
500,000,000	Reef communities collapse.
450,000,000	Corals and coralline algae appear for the first time, and the reef is rebuilt.
350,000,000	A period of retrenchment.
225,000,000	Reef communities devastated for the second time. The world loses about half of its animals and plants.
200,000,000	The first appearance of modern corals and zooxanthellae.
70,000,000	Reef communities suffer the third and last major collapse (at the same time the dinosaurs were wiped out).
1,500,000	Modern ice ages begin.

Occasionally, the continental shoreline on which the barrier reef was built may be lifted up by tectonic forces originating in the mantle of the earth. When this happens the reef may be left standing high and dry, where we can see it. One example of this is a reef that was built 250 million years ago and which now forms a mountainous ridge of jagged rock nearly 650 kilometres long surrounding the Delaware Basin on the border between Texas and New Mexico. A sixty-five kilometre exposed section of the reef is the famous El Capitan in the Guadeloupe Mountains, the face of which stands more than a thousand metres high.

water, and the maximum concentration of oxygen. They are themselves protected from the pounding of the waves, because they are flat and cemented solidly to the underlying "coralline rock." They are so flat, and so tightly cemented down, that they don't look the least bit like a plant, but like a smear of yellow, pink or purple on the limestone.

These algae grow quickly in the favourable conditions found on the outer face of the reef top, rapidly adding layers to the limestone platform. Additional layers increase the width of the reef fringing the shoreline. Gradually the ridge of calcium-secreting algae marches offshore. The death of corals, clams, snails and other creatures that have calcareous skeletons results in the erosion of their skeletons into a beautiful white and pink sand that falls into the basin left behind by the ridge of calcareous algae moving outward and upward. The sand is piled up and trapped between the living corals and cemented into place. This cementing or lithification goes on continuously, although no one is yet sure how it works. The same type of sand also falls forward and creates a sloping front to the offshore face of the coralline algal ridge, where corals on the outer slope trap this falling debris between them. There the sand is cemented into place to form a surface on which new growth can be initiated. Over many thousands of years, the slow movement of the ridge of calcareous algae away from the shoreline, combined with the continuous rain of sand both to the inside of the reef top, where it forms a shallow basin, and to the outside of the reef top, where it falls into the ocean depths to build a sloping front or fore reef, creates a barrier that can be gigantic, and may seem to rise up out of the ocean floor many kilometres offshore. These majestic formations can be very old indeed, often millions of years old.

Chapter Two
The Living Reef

Early explorers described the reef using images of underwater gardens or forests. They spoke of constant motion, the swaying branches of tree-like living things under the water, and they sometimes compared the reef with its bird-like fishes to a young forest alive with finches and sparrows in the summer. Other parts of the reef appeared stiff and unmoving, and looked like some exotic scrubland. Dominant colours in the shallow waters were the same greens and browns of our dry world, although like airborne birds and butterflies, the fishes were often garishly coloured, standing out in bold contrast to the surrounding muted tones.

But the underwater trees are not plants, and the watery scrublands are not plant-covered. The plants on the reef are mostly tiny, or hidden. A few are large, but they are often hard to find unless you know exactly the right places to look. The frozen scrub-bushes, the swaying branches and the stiffened trunks, are all animals. Even the "ground," with its lumpy boulders, is alive. The reef is a topsy-turvy and alien world where the animals are often fixed and stationary, and the plants sometimes move around. Those first ancient, seedless plants that began the reef could not respond to the underwater opportunities and create an equivalent of our terrestrial forest. Instead the animals responded to that opportunity, and once they became dominant they were never replaced.

What are those animals that look like trees and grass? Many are the descendants of the first animals to invade the ancient stromatolite

OPPOSITE: *One of the commonest forms sponges take is that of a tube. Like all sponges, tube sponges feed by drawing water in through pores in the outer wall, sieving plankton from it, and expelling it out through the large opening at the top of the tube.*

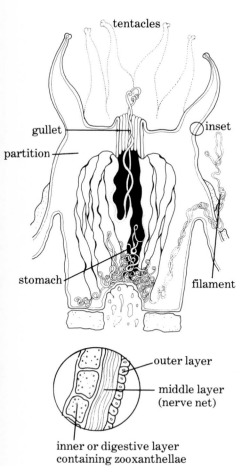

tentacles

gullet — inset

partition —

stomach — filament

outer layer

middle layer
(nerve net)

inner or digestive layer
containing zooxanthellae

Anatomy of a coral polyp

plant-reefs of Paleozoic times, the sponges. After eons of evolution, the sponges have become very specialized and varied creatures, as different one from another as are the birds from mammals. On a reef, sponges vary in size from microscopic to so large that several divers can easily rest inside the bowl-shaped opening. Some are flat and slimy to the touch, some are shaped like tubes or candles, some are misshapen lumpy excrescences, others are exotic and delicately branched. Some reef sponges are soft and squishy, but many have little glass-like inclusions (spicules) in them. The brilliant red or "fire" sponges have a chemical that acts as a powerful irritant, causing sensations of burning. Other sponges feel like the old leather of a shoe. Some sponges are grey-brown, but many are bright hues of red, orange, purple and green, although why they should have these colours is unknown.

Whatever their colouration, shape or size, all sponges are simple creatures. They have no true "tissues" like our skin or muscle and consist of only three or four types of cells. One forms a thin outer layer of flat cells and a second forms an inner layer of specialized cells, each with a collar, out of the centre of which protrudes a tiny whip or flagellum which lashes about creating a current of water. Most sponges also have microscopic holes or pores all over their outer surfaces. The sponge is filled with hollow sections that lead to one or several large openings to the outside. The tiny, beating whips push water out through the openings, which causes more water to be sucked in through the tiny pores. The collared cells and their little whips are also the food-gathering part of the sponge. Minute food particles are trapped in the collar by the whip and then engulfed by the rest of the cell. A third cell type acts as a distribution unit, taking excess food to the outer layer of cells.

As reef builders, sponges are important because the debris and sand that are trapped between them and corals make up the largest bulk of the reef structure. In a very special group of sponges, mechanisms of attacking and drilling into coral skeletons have evolved. In certain deeper water zones on most reefs, sponges are as abundant as the corals.

Corals are the single most important reef builder. They may not contribute the most limestone to the reef (on some reefs, calcareous algae produce more calcium carbonate than corals) and their living tissue may be a mere skim of stiff jelly on the top of that limestone base, but they are essential to almost all reef growth. For many centuries they were thought to be plants, and the first man to suggest they were animals, Jean André Peyssonel in 1723, was ridiculed and disgraced until he became completely discouraged and quit the scientific profession forever. But he was right about corals, and since then, it has been found that corals are only one kind of a very large and extremely varied group of related animals. Sea anemones, jellyfish, siphonophores, like the Portuguese Man-of-War, sea whips, sea fans, colonial hydroids, gorgonians and even the delicate sea pansies are all near-relatives of the corals.

Curios sold in tourist or pet stores as corals, are usually only the

cleaned and dried skeletons of corals. The original animal is dead and
has been washed away. But even what remains is very beautiful and
an array of coral skeletons will demonstrate the range of shapes they
can achieve. Most of those sold in shops are small and shaped like
boulders. Close examination reveals an intricate structure of raised,
delicate, white leaves or stars on the surface. Sometimes the pattern is
of individual leaf clusters in a circle, or of meandering hills and valleys.
When these corals with wandering valleys on their surfaces are also
round boulders, they are often called "brain corals" because of the
similarity of the convolutions to those of a human brain. Branching
forms may resemble some majestic elk horn, or juniper hedge. Tourist
shops rarely sell the most impressive corals because they are so huge.
A single coral colony may be twice the size of a living room. Such a
coral is usually massive and heavy, but will often have leafy shelving
edges, a delicacy somehow not incongruous with the underwater
environment.

Underwater, corals look much the same as in the shop except they
are not white. They range in colour from greens and browns to
startling purples and mauves. Underwater they feel hard, but slippery
or slimy to the touch, whereas outside the water they become dry and
sharp. The reason for this is that underwater you are actually putting
your hand on the live coral polyp, a thin layer of slippery stuff that is
the living animal responsible for building the rocks that comprise the
reef.

It is difficult to peer closely enough through a diver's face mask to
see the detail of a coral polyp, but if you were to look at it through a
microscope, you would see a ring of tentacles surrounding the edge of
the polyp. The tentacles are usually fairly short, flexible or unjointed
arm-like projections, that often end in a little ball, or taper to a sharp
point. In corals the tentacles are found in multiples of six, and all of the
little circular limestone cups of the skeleton also have leaf-like flanges
or ridges around the lips arranged in multiples of six. The body of the
polyp is a short, hollow cylinder rising up off the limestone cup. This is
the part of the coral that has colour in it and the pigment is contained
in the outer layer of tissue.

There are only three layers of tissue in the polyp. The outer layer
has several different types of cells, including sense cells that react to a
variety of things such as knocks, bangs, and changes in light intensity,
and then direct muscle cells to relax or contract. The messages they
transmit are carried along a nerve net which is found in the middle
layer of tissue. Also on the outside of the polyp are special cells armed
for combat and the capture of food. Each of these cells has a tiny hair
sticking straight out which acts like a trigger. If anything touches the
hair, a microscopic spring-loaded thread-like arrow is fired. In some
types, even the current caused by a small creature swimming past can
detonate the device.

An extraordinary mechanism is required to make these
nematocysts or little bombs work. When the tiny hairs are disturbed,
water is released into the mechanism, forcing the fine, coiled filament
to turn inside-out as it is driven outward into the water. These can

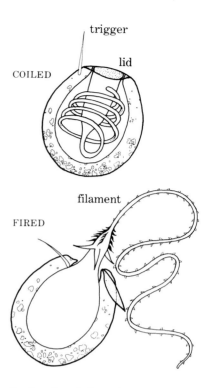

*Spring-loaded, coiled darts,
or nematocysts, fired by a
hair trigger, found in coral
tentacles and filaments, are
used to capture prey.*

explode outward with real force to penetrate the hard shells of small crustaceans. Many of the hollow filaments contain a poison which can be injected into the wound, immobilizing the prey. Not all of the nematocysts work by penetration—some are sticky, or are designed to wrap around little hairs and legs of the prey, others are real lassos. Once the prey is captured, the tentacles pass it to the mouth.

If the coral polyp is swallowed by another animal, often the nematocysts do not fire. One sea creature, related to the land slugs which eat the lettuce in our gardens, purposely eats corals so that it can arm itself with the stolen slings and arrows. The nematocysts grow into place in the skin of the sea slug and continue to function as if they were in the polyp of the coral.

If you look down on a coral polyp through a microscope, the ring of tentacles is seen to surround a small opening. This "mouth" or gullet is a short muscular tube leading into the main body cavity.

The third and innermost layer of cells is the digestive layer, which provides nourishment for all the other cells in the coral's body. The most abundant cell in this layer secretes enzymes which are used to digest the captured prey. Partitions ridge the inside of the coral polyp's "stomach," and the thin edges of these partitions are elongated into thread-like filaments. If your microscopic view continued inside you would see these filaments as a pile of spaghetti. The filaments are loaded with nematocysts and digestive cells. Surprisingly, the filaments are sometimes seen sticking out of the coral's mouth, and even at times through the body wall. In some corals they are used to gather food which the tentacles have shot and killed, but failed to transfer to the mouth. On the partitions that line the polyp's digestive layer are extremely tiny hairs called cilia, which beat constantly to create currents of water ensuring that all the food particles are swept about and found by the digestive cells of the partitions or filaments. In some species of corals, the food is also transported to the mouth using

long strips of extruded mucus, which become coated with particles of food and debris.

In water which has become unusually dirty, or which has a substance in it that the coral senses is harmful, all corals may exude copious amounts of mucus as a defensive mechanism, coating the outer layer of tissue against contact with the noxious substance, and to carry away extra material or debris that may have fallen on it. Divers may notice on occasion that the water seems full of silt carried on long translucent strings—the result of mucus secretion by the corals.

The skeleton of corals is formed by the outer layer of tissue near the base of the polyp. A flat plate of calcium carbonate is laid down and then the outer layer of tissue is creased into radial folds that also contain layers of calcium carbonate. This creates vertical walls that rise from the plate skeletons. The small spaces in the polyp's outer layer of tissue contain minute crystals of aragonite, a fibrous crystalline form of calcium carbonate. These crystals are then extruded right through the cell wall onto the skeleton.

Because corals do not survive well in an aquarium it has always been extremely difficult to study their calcium-depositing mechanism. Modern researchers have moved the studies underwater onto the reef, where, using radioactive calcium, they have been able to measure the growth rate of many species. Corals usually grow from one to ten centimetres per year, the fastest-growing corals being the branching types such as elkhorn. Years ago it was discovered that corals grew ten to fifteen times faster in the daytime than at night. Growth rate is so sensitive to changes in light level that on a cloudy day, the rate of growth is less than half the rate on a bright sunny day.

The key to the coral's rapid growth lies hidden in the inner layer of the coral polyp's body, right within the digestive sac or "stomach" wall, where there are cells that contain green, living plant cells. Because the outer and middle layers of the coral polyp are nearly transparent, the plant cells receive light which they need to be able to grow. It was a subject of much speculation and debate, when they were first discovered, what these plant cells were doing in the coral, and theories ranged from describing them as parasites to accidental inclusions. It was observed that if the corals were kept in the dark for an extended period of time, the number of these little plant cells in the polyp declined, until finally there were none or very few. A clever scientist then isolated the coral so the plant cells could not get back in, and turned the lights on. The rate of growth of the coral did not increase. The conclusion was obvious: the little plant cells, which are called zooxanthellae, were responsible in some way for the rapid growth of the coral. They were not parasites, but in scientific terms were symbionts, meaning that the plants were living in the coral and deriving some benefit for themselves. They in turn contributed to the welfare and success of the corals. The corals could grow much faster with the help of the zooxanthellae, and the coral polyp provided a good place for the plants to hide from predators, while allowing sunlight to reach the plant cells. Because corals are animals, they breathe oxygen from the water and give off carbon dioxide, which is then used by the

OPPOSITE: *Gorgonians, close relatives of corals and anemones, are formed by branching colonies of polyps. In this close-up view of a branch tip the details of each polyp can be discerned.*

OPPOSITE: *Alcyonarians are found in a bewildering array of shapes and colours on all coral reefs. The soft coral form, which is found only very rarely in the Caribbean, is abundant throughout the Indo-Pacific and Red Sea areas. This species was photographed in shallow water on a western Pacific atoll.*

Another of the many different types of alcyonarians is the gorgonian family, of which a typical member is the sea fan. It orients itself so that its flexible lattice structure faces into the prevailing currents.

plant cells. Similarly, being in the digestive cells, the plant cells are able to absorb the nutrients they need.

It has taken many years to determine how the increased growth of the corals is made possible by the action of the little plant cells. Calcium is an element that is present in all sea water, and because the polyp is full of sea water, calcium is available to the polyp, if it has a way of trapping it. In the skeleton of the coral, calcium is deposited as calcium carbonate. The carbonate part of the limestone comes from the "exhaled" carbon dioxide of the corals. But it is not possible to add carbon dioxide directly to calcium dissolved in water and get calcium carbonate. Corals produce an enzyme called carbonic anhydrase which by combining water and carbon dioxide creates an acid called carbonic acid. In sea water, the carbonic acid rapidly breaks down into bicarbonate and carbonate ions.

The plant cells' activities raise the concentration of carbonate ions in the cell, and also increase the pH (makes it more alkaline). The coral, "preferring" to have the pH the way it was, responds by depositing these excess carbonate ions combined with calcium to produce calcium carbonate, thereby adding to its external skeleton.

The more the plant cells fix carbon dioxide in the body of the coral, the higher the concentration of carbonate ions gets, and the faster the coral binds it to the calcium, piling the resulting calcium carbonate onto the floor outside its body. Because photosynthesis depends on sunlight, the more light that falls on the zooxanthellae in the coral, the faster it can deposit calcium carbonate.

This remarkable mechanism explains why the corals which form reefs are only found in shallow water, where they enjoy bright light. It also explains why the corals around a sinking island must be able to grow upwards to the shallow water. Without the symbiotic plant-coral relationship, the rate of growth is reduced by more than ninety per cent.

Essentially the same body plan and life history is true of another major group of animals that make up the underwater seascape on a reef. Gorgonians and alcyonarians are composed of colonies of polyps, but the tentacles and parts are divided into groups of eight, rather than six. Symbiotic zooxanthellae also assist these to maintain very high rates of growth. The skeleton, which is flexible, and sways with the passing water currents, is not made of calcium carbonate and seems to be on the inside of the animals, rather than on the outside as it is in the corals. The supporting stems of the tree-like gorgonians are made of a type of horny material, found along the inner, central axis the way wood is inside the bark of a tree. In this case, however, the "bark" is composed of individual polyps of the gorgonian colony growing around the stem, which is actually secreted by the outer skin of the polyp. Sea fans and sea whips also belong to this group.

One of the most famous of the corals, which is actually not a true coral, is the "fire coral." If touched, the sting of its powerful nematocysts will cause an instant and startling burning sensation. The nematocysts can easily pierce the skin of a human, injecting poisons which create the burning sensation. Fire corals have two types of polyps. The most abundant is long and slender and has tentacles armed with the powerful nematocysts, and surrounds in a ring, a short rounded polyp with a mouth. The slender polyps capture the prey and hand it to the central polyp for digestion. Although they are separate individuals, the polyps are interconnected members of a colony which co-operate, sharing the duties and rewards. The coral skeleton is made of calcium carbonate and these polyps also benefit from the co-operation of zooxanthellae to speed their growth rate.

In addition to the role that the zooxanthellae play on the reef, there are two other major groups of plants that are essential to the rapid and constant growth of the reef structure. Certain forms of green and the red algae have developed methods of depositing calcium carbonate from the sea onto the reef bottom. Both of these types of algae are quite primitive, but capable of surprisingly rapid rates of growth. To a diver, the most obvious of these are the green algae. They look like seaweeds, but instead of feeling slimy, they feel gritty, and in some cases, even brittle.

One of the most common of the brittle forms, and one which contributes prodigious amounts of limestone sand to the reef, is a plant

Close relatives of gorgonians, which occur in deep parts of coral reefs, are the "precious" and "black" corals. Both lack zooxanthellae. Precious corals are a very beautiful orange-pink colour. Like black coral they are often dredged to make "coral" jewellery.

Portuguese Man-of-War, which look something like a jellyfish, are near relatives of the fire corals. The nematocysts that these creatures possess are so powerful that they can capture full-grown fish such as a mackerel, and a bad sting from one can be fatal to humans.

called *Halimeda*. It stands on a small stalk, flaring from the low stem to form a fan. The branches of this fan are made up of small limey plates joined together in a line. The whole plant is rarely as much as thirty centimetres high, but it is a mistake to judge the importance of an animal or plant by the size it reaches, or by the number of them that can be seen at any one time, without paying attention to the speed at which they grow, reproduce and die. The growth of *Halimeda* is extremely rapid and as the little plates reach the end of the branches, they fall off, to form a coarse sand under the plant. Growth is so fast that the plant would soon bury itself, except that it grows upward on top of the increasing pile of little plates collecting below. On many healthy reefs, where this is an abundant species, there are vast sand plains in the lagoons where the dominant part of the sandy bottom is composed of the little plates of *Halimeda*. The plant grows most commonly right in amongst the corals.

Another of the green coralline algae that grows in reef coral environments is the "sea bottle." Beachcombers will be familiar with the little stiff and translucent bags of sea water that wash up on the shore after a storm. Underwater they can be found like little Christmas tree decorations tucked into upturned crevices in the corals. Another unusually shaped form is the "merman's shaving brush," which looks like a green shaving brush with a sandy handle.

The importance of green algae as a reef builder, despite the impressive efforts of plants like *Halimeda*, is overshadowed by the coralline red algae. In some parts of the world, particularly in the Orient and in the Philippines, but also North America, other types of red algae are harvested as a commercial food crop. None of the reef-building red algae, however, would be useful as a food product, as they are much too heavily invested with calcium carbonate. In fact, they really do not look much like plants in many cases. Often they resemble misshapen lumps of oddly coloured rock, and seem to be found in the least accessible, wave-torn area on the top of a reef.

Reef-building red algae are often confused with dead corals. However, the surface does not have the same finely ridged and sectioned structure, all in multiples of six, that is characteristic of the corals. Instead, the pastel-hued limestone surface seems to be either continuous and smooth, or filled with minute pores. Unlike live corals they are not slimy to the touch, and they do not sting like the fire corals.

It would be a mistake to assume that because red algae are relatively inconspicuous they are unimportant. These plants are sprinters in the production of limestone on the reef. Often the cementing algae that are found on the reef tops are producing limestone much faster than the corals themselves, creating the coralline sand that is trapped between the sponges, coral and gorgonians growing both seaward and shoreward of the reef top.

Rates of growth are difficult to measure, especially if they are slow. The submerged wrecks of ships can demonstrate in a dramatic and beautiful, if expensive and occasionally tragic way, just how fast different species grow. Since the times of the early explorers, reefs have been a hazard to the mariner. When the hulls were made of wood, the wrecked ship rapidly disintegrated or was eaten by the reef creatures. In recent years, ships' hulls have been made of metal, and although the metal rusts, it may take years to disintegrate. Ships wrecked on reefs provide an "experimental" surface that will remain in one piece long enough for corals to become established and grow. If the wreck can be identified and the exact time it has been in the water determined, the minimum rates of growth can be estimated. For example, if a diver swimming over a wreck finds a piece of brain coral forty centimetres across growing on the deck of a ship that has been down for forty years, the coral must have grown at least one centimetre per year.

Wrecks provide another insight into the natural course of events on a reef. By watching and cataloguing the sequence of the colonizers on the wreck, it has been found that there is a predictable series of types of animals and plants to appear. Experiments done in the sea by disturbing the natural assemblage of reef species confirms that the reef community attempts to reassemble itself by starting at an appropriate level in the sequence from early colonizing forms and then working its way back to a full reef. For a minor change in the reef community, it does not take more than a decade, but for a major reduction in the community, the reassembly may take a very long time.

One of the potentially most destructive factors that constantly threatens to disturb this natural assemblage that has taken so long to build up is the force of the ocean waves crashing on the reef. It is the very nature of the reef to resist the force of these waves, and of the erosion that they can cause. Indeed they do more than resist the waves, they throw them back from the mountain or continental shoreline, as a natural breakwater. While the strongest and most massive concrete and steel structures that we put out to break the force of the waves will ultimately succumb and crumble, some reefs seem to grow stronger with each wave. The secret for the reef is not to resist the water, but to thwart and divert its energy like an expert swordsman, who, with a minimum of effort, catches the onrushing blade and slightly changes the direction of the rush so that it slices harmlessly to the side.

Viewed from an airplane, the front of an atoll or fully developed barrier reef facing the waves has an oddly jagged appearance, as if

OPPOSITE: *Although sponges are among the most primitive multi-cellular animals, the basket sponge can grow to a very large size, up to two metres across.*

Coral reefs thwart the destructive energy of onrushing ocean waves by channelling them into small, vertical-walled canyons which are called surge channels.

coralline teeth were bared to the open sea in a permanent snarl. Each of the teeth is actually a very large, triangular buttress of coral, pointing offshore towards the incoming wave. At the offshore tip, the point of the buttress begins to cut into the wave like the cutting edge of a wedge. Between the wedges are canyons that become gradually narrower and shallower towards the base of the wedges, until the canyon is a narrow, shallow trough little more than a groove where the bases of the buttresses are joined together. The shallowest part of the canyon and the widest part of the bases form a ridge, parallel to the shore, over which the waves break.

The ridge is a wild place to try to study. One moment it is nearly dry, but the sucking of water from retreating waves threatens to drag you away. The next moment, a wave thunders towards you, and in a crash, the world seems to disappear in milk-white foam. During the quiet seconds, you can see that the ridge is mostly coralline red algae, not coral. It is very different from the rest of the reef. Low-growing, lumpy and encrusting life-forms dominate.

A few daring scientists have fought their way in and out of the foam that fills the canyon between the buttresses in an attempt to see what is there. They have found that the shallow parts of the valley are often scoured, and have boulders rolling in them, but the walls and slightly deeper parts are alive with coral and algae. On the tops of the buttresses, the growth gradually changes from being predominantly algae to a mixture of algae and coral and then to mostly coral at the front or cutting edge.

The oncoming wave, though split, still has almost all of its energy,

Buttress and groove formation on a fringing reef.

and begins to rush up the canyon, which becomes progressively both narrower and shallower. The water is gently directed into a narrower stream headed upward, and by the time it is at the wedge, the reef has parried the thrust of the wave away from itself and up into the air over the ridge so that much of the force of the waves is lost in its fall. It is still a powerful force, as anyone will tell you who has tried to walk or swim in the area where the waves crash down, but the bulk of the wave is directed between coral buttresses without ever really touching the reef top. Beyond this, towards the shore, the wave is hardly felt as more than a gentle rise and fall of water level.

In addition to the buttress and canyon arrangement, reefs further thwart the destructive efforts of waves by the mass of crevices and hollows in the reef front. Corals on the top of buttresses have close, thick branches, and on the walls they are shelving, leaving furrows and horizontal gulleys. As the water pushes against this porous wall, it is diverted into many directions. The resulting friction reduces the energy of the moving water mass very quickly. The canyons which carry the wedged waves also carry away much of the limestone sand that is generated by the erosive forces. This sand slides down the outer face of the reef, where it is trapped and cemented into place.

Fringing reefs also have a buttress and groove formation to resist the action of the waves, but because atolls and barrier reefs have vertical walls and a better developed ridge, the reef top is shallower than that in fringing reefs. Usually, however, the shallowest part of the fringing reef is a little different because it is an early phase of what is really a continuous chain of stages, so it is difficult to give an all encompassing description of what the reef top of all fringing reefs looks like. As well, in many of the popular tropical Caribbean islands, for instance, the impact of the shallow-water snorkeler collecting curios, or the effect of indiscriminate dumping of sewage and refuse, has recently caused the loss of much of the shallowest parts as living entities.

The essential architectural difference between fringing and barrier or atoll reefs is the lack of a well-defined wave-breaking ridge in fringing reefs. Its shallowest part is usually a line of elkhorn and

Staghorn coral is commonly found in large thickets in shallow-water fringing reefs in the Caribbean.

staghorn coral, thick branching types that grow faster than any other species and form vast thickets of impenetrable spiky branches, up to several hundred metres wide, paralleling the shore for kilometres. Elkhorn, the heavier of the two, gives way on the seaward edge of this line to the spindly, spiked staghorn. As the waves pass through the thicket, they are slowed, but not stopped. These corals tend to break apart relatively easily, and erosive forces break them down into sand which drifts down the slope. In many fringing reefs, the elkhorn line grows thickly to about ten metres, but staghorn thickets continue to fifteen metres or more. From these thickets, a gradually sloping coral and sponge-covered bottom continues down the fore reef to a maximum of about twenty metres.

The buttress and groove formations begin to form at this level, but the shoreward and embryonic "ridge" is still not much more than a sandy plane. Growing outward towards the sea are the wedge-shaped coral buttresses alternating with sand-covered valleys. Even at this depth, they serve to dissipate the mechanical energy of the waves, and to allow the flow of fine sands down the reef front into the deeper sections of the reef. On the fringing reef's buttress formations are found a variety of reef corals. Those at the bottom of the buttress and up the sides tend to be massive, but because they have zooxanthellae and need to make the most of the reduced amount of light that reaches them, the growth form alters and spreads into shelves, reaching out from the sides of the wall like grotesquely overgrown cabbage leaves. On the tops of the buttresses the form is a more familiar boulder shape that resists the waves and brings the maximum amount of surface into view of the light without sacrificing strength. In time, the developing buttresses and valleys increase in size until they and the elkhorn thickets join.

On all reefs, the whole of the area seaward of the reef-top ridge to the drop-off is considered to be the fore reef. On an atoll or barrier reef, it is often quite a small area, whereas on a fringing reef, it can be extensive. On an atoll, the drop-off is a very dramatic feature beginning in shallow water just below the buttress zone on the windward side of the islands. As the name suggests, it is characterized by a sudden increase in slope from relatively gentle to very rapid. Usually, the wall is vertical or nearly so, and sometimes it is actually undercut. It is an eerie feeling to hang suspended over nearly a thousand metres of empty water, looking down the wall of coral into a blue-black darkness. Shelves formed by gorgonians or corals reach out into the clear water to capture the sunlight as it filters down to their depths. Most reefs drop off at between five and thirty metres deep, and on atolls the walls may continue down for literally a thousand metres without reaching a "bottom." In most barrier reefs the bottom is shallower, because of the way in which the reef was formed. In either case, it is usually too deep to see the bottom of the slope from the top of the drop-off.

Shoreward of the wave-breaking ridge is the lagoon. Lagoons are not always found on fringing reefs, particularly on new ones, but are always a part of atolls, and barrier reefs. Most of the lagoon is a sandy plain, the result of accumulated sand from the algae and corals that have died and been eroded into smaller bits. In the shallow water scattered domes of coral rise up from the bottom—small isolated patches of coral, sponges and gorgonians that have found a solid place somewhere in the shifting sands of the lagoon and managed to anchor themselves. The patches of coral are sometimes tall, undercut spires that look like mushrooms measuring thirty to fifty metres across the cap. Other patches spread many hectares in area. Compared to the corals on the outer reef, the species on patch reefs are often delicate, fragile things. The massive lumpy coralline algae are much less common here, and are replaced by branching green algae like *Halimeda*.

Lagoons are also characterized by the presence of large underwater fields of eelgrass or turtlegrass. These plants are not algae, but are seed-bearing, flowering plants that have re-invaded the sea. They are not limestone producers but have root systems that trap sand (algae do not have root systems). Although they grow to a height of only a few centimetres, they grow extremely rapidly and are an important addition to the lagoon community, which, except for the patch reefs and grass beds, seems essentially like a desert, in contrast to the dynamic and active outer reef.

While most of the living things apparent on a coral reef are animals, one of the most important seaweeds is a green alga called Halimeda *which has the ability to deposit limestone in its "leaves."*

In Caribbean barrier reefs, the drop off meets the sea floor at a depth of between 60 and 150 metres. It is an unexplained fact that Caribbean reef corals grow actively to depths of 100 metres in clear water, whereas in the Pacific, corals cease active growth at about 60 metres, where the predominant forms are sponges and gorgonians, including the precious black corals.

Chapter Three
The Reef Food Web

The plants and animals on a coral reef are more than a random assortment of odds and ends. Although it must seem like a chaotic riot of colours and shapes for the first-time visitor, a careful observer can see patterns to the reef's architecture and to the coral species that make up the reef. Forces create and maintain a system of creatures to withstand the opposing forces that are trying to reduce it to randomness.

Forces acting to break down the reef system include the sinking of the mountainous base of the reef, and waves crashing down to erode and crumble the structure to a flat plain. It takes work and energy to resist these destructive forces. Because the reef is a biological system, the energy is contained in and used by the animals and plants that make up the reef.

Where the creatures get their energy and how they use it is the subject of a science which has the now-familiar name of "ecology," a word coined to describe the study of the inter-relationships between living things in their natural habitat. Very quickly scientists discovered that while there are many different kinds of plant and animal communities, they all share a common feature: they use energy to grow, move, heal wounds and reproduce, and all of this energy is derived from the food they eat.

Getting energy from food is not a simple process. Digestion only breaks it down into a usable form; it does not actually release the energy. To do that the animal must combine the food it has broken down in digestion with oxygen from breathing. The simplest and most important process, respiration, reduces one of the food products (sugar) into two others — a gas (carbon dioxide) and water, releasing energy. Energy that comes from breaking down sugar molecules goes into muscle movement, repairing damage, and building new tissues — the activities that resist the breakdown of the reef system.

Tracing back through a chain of "who ate whom" leads to plants as a beginning. For more than a century, it has been known that sunlighted plants produce oxygen. Because of the presence of a peculiar green pigment called chlorophyll, plants are able to catch the sunlight and somehow store the energy in their tissues. This reaction is called photosynthesis and it is almost the exact reverse of respiration. In both respiration and photosynthesis, a highly unstable, phosphate-rich molecule ATP (adenosine triphosphate) acts to transfer the sun's energy which is stored in the sugar molecule. The sugar molecule becomes the major warehouse of energy for all plant activities, and is undoubtedly one of the most abundant chemicals produced by any process on earth. Literally billions of tons of sugar are manufactured by plants.

Sunlight is used to generate sugar molecules in plants, and almost all of the energy that animals have is derived from plants. If all plants disappeared, no new energy would be available to animals, and after they had used up all their stored energy, they would die. It would take longest for the effect to reach the predators (animal eaters) because they do not eat plants directly, but eventually they too would run out of other animals to eat.

Ecologists have given names to the various players in this game of life, according to what they do, and what they eat. Plants are called producers, because of all the living things on earth, they are the only ones that produce energy and living tissue from the raw materials of the earth and its envelope of gases. With one known exception, all of the energy available for all animals must first come from the sun through plants, and animals must consume these plants to get their energy. For this reason, animals in the food chain are called consumers. Some of the consuming animals eat only plants (herbivores), others eat only animals (carnivores) and still others eat a mixture (omnivores). Within this classification we distinguish different levels of carnivores. Those that feed only on herbivores are called first-level carnivores. Some that feed on first-level carnivores are called second-level carnivores, and a few third-level carnivores feed only on carnivores that have fed on carnivores. Top predators are those that are themselves virtually immune to predation. As the energy is moved along this food chain, much of it is used up by each level of consumer through inefficiency in digesting food, and energy used up in growth, movement and reproduction. The community must be adjusted so that herbivores do not eat all of the plants; there must be some left to reproduce and provide more young plants.

Of the energy striking the earth from the sun, most is reflected back out into space, some heats the earth's surface, and only a small amount actually hits the leaves, or photosynthetic parts of the plants.

In 1977, a dramatic discovery was made in the depths of the ocean, where no sunlight penetrates. A unique community of living creatures in the absence of sunlight has been able to trap energy from the sulphur-rich hot water and debris that surround cracks in the ocean floor. These cracks are heated by molten lava oozing up from the earth's core. Replacements for plants in this community are a type of bacteria that can use sulphur to trap energy in chemical bonds. These bacteria also make sugars, but no one yet knows for sure what the mechanisms are. The community has existed for a very long time, because there are species of animals in it that grow nowhere else, and therefore must have evolved in this deep, dark, hot, sulphurous and salty environment, under the crushing pressures of tons of water.

Only about half of that is incorporated into the plant's tissue, and of this amount, no more than fifteen per cent of the plant tissue is eventually consumed by animals and transferred into animal tissue. This means that to get 15 kilograms of herbivores in a community, you must begin with at least 100 kilograms of plants. Carnivores are even less efficient: about 90 per cent of the energy is used in other activities. From 15 kilograms of herbivores, therefore, there would be 1.5 kilograms of first-level carnivores, 0.15 kilograms of second-level carnivores and a vanishingly small amount of top predator, 0.015 kilograms. To put it another way, to support a 150-kilogram shark would require 1,000,000 kilograms of plants.

When these animals or plants die, there is a host of tiny organisms ready to move in and decompose the creatures to get the remaining energy. In the end all the energy is gone forever back into space as waste heat of a very low grade. It has been used up in the activities of chasing prey, reproducing, repairing wounds and a host of other necessary functions. Energy may be lost forever from the earth, but the raw materials plants use to create themselves are never lost. Usually there are vast numbers of tiny creatures taking the refuse from the community and turning it into the raw materials for more plant growth, more producers.

All of these principles are to be found on the coral reef, a world under the water that contains producers, herbivores and carnivores. The reef has its leafy plants browsed by underwater "deer." Jackals, lions and tigers of the blue lurk in underwater groves for the unwary, just as they do on land. Profound differences in the types of animals and plants that have these roles under the water impose equally great differences in the kinds of tricks they must use for hiding from predators, or for getting swiftly out of the way.

The environment itself has unique characteristics forcing creatures to adopt certain habits. Water, for instance, is nearly eight hundred times as dense as air, so while it is much more difficult to move through it at any speed, it is much easier to remain hovering in the water than it is in the air. It is unusual to be able to see more than seventy-five to one hundred metres, even in magnificently clear water, yet if the same were true of air, it would barely be possible to see the far end of a football field. While air temperature on a typical, tropical sunny day might vary from a high of 40°C to a low of 23°C at night, a few metres away in the water, the temperature of the water over the reef is unlikely to vary more than one or two degrees from an average of 28°C or 30°C. Reef creatures, therefore, do not have to find elaborate protection from extremes of temperature. On the other hand, water is not nearly as rich in supplying oxygen for breathing. Oxygen comprises about 20 per cent of the air, whereas it is usually no more than 0.0015 per cent of the water. Getting oxygen is always a much more critical problem for water creatures.

For most algae, the buoyant effect of the water is crucial. Unlike land plants, they do not have stiff stems to hold them erect, but instead are held aloft in the blue clarity simply because they are a little lighter than water. They have no roots because there is no need to be

OPPOSITE: *Grotesquely shaped, large spider crabs come out of hiding at night, using their spoon-shaped claws to feed on seaweed.*

Although vital to the reef community, blue-green algae are also thought to be the source of a very virulent poison. Ciguatera, a disease that causes great agony and often death in humans, results from eating large predatory fishes that have eaten smaller herbivores which fed on blue-green algae.

One species of algae, the "sea grape" or *Caulerpa* (not to be confused with the tree of the same common name), looks delicious, but is poisonous. This plant creeps along the bottom, and along its ten to thirty centimetre length produces clusters of what look for all the world like fine, green California grapes.

firmly anchored to the ground, nor is there any need to draw moisture or nourishment from underlying sediments, as terrestrial plants do. The algae can drink the nourishment from the surrounding water through their bodies, so they have what are called holdfasts, or little anchors, rather than a root system. Many underwater plants move freely with water currents or waves, washing back and forth in a way that would destroy a land plant.

The least conspicuous algae that can still be seen with the naked eye are those that belong to the most primitive group, the "blue-green" algae. Most of these are single-celled plants attached to other plants, but a few grow together in tiny chains. To a diver, they look like fine, gossamer strands of filmy, dark-green hair. Or they may form a thin grey-green or even reddish-coloured mat over the sand in quiet lagoons. Although inconspicuous, they are important to the reef because they trap a great deal of nitrogen, a nutrient important to the success of the community.

The most common forms of the less primitive "green" algae come in long, thread-like filaments that look like hair, or in branched filaments which look a bit like a tangled mop. If they are present in large amounts on a reef, this may mean something is amiss. The reef may have been recently disturbed, reducing the number of creatures that eat algae. A species of green algae that is sometimes seen in some abundance on a reef is sea lettuce. These are the same grass-green colour, but instead of being filamentous, they are very thin sheets, a single cell thick, and look just like lettuce that has been in the refrigerator too long. Underwater, buoyed up, they have a beautiful undulating grace.

Although "brown" algae are more important in the north than in the tropics, they are one of the most abundant algae forms in the world's oceans. *Sargassum*, the famous floating seaweed, is not at all delicate, but has a firm stem and leaf with little turgid balls distributed along its length. The little balls are filled with gas and are a flotation mechanism. Some species of *Sargassum* are found only in the Sargasso Sea, a body of ocean east of Florida nearly half a million square kilometres in extent. Others, however, are found on the reefs where they resemble strands of northern kelp. Most attached forms also live quite well as fragments floating around free from the bottom. Attached *Sargassum* never reaches the size of northern kelp, but still can be over one metre in length. Other tropical brown algae are smaller, but can be abundant, particularly in lagoon areas. Large patches are found on coral rubble and beach rock along beaches near fringing reefs. One of the most common on the reef is a small, purple-coloured brown algae that branches uniformly in twos, forming a dense carpet (*Dictyota*). Most people never notice the plant because of the way it blends in with the complex background of the reef.

Several kinds of "red" algae are feathery or leaf-like, but others feel like bean sprouts. While most of the red algae on the reef deposit calcium carbonate in their tissues, a great variety are not coralline, and are succulent enough to be eaten by people. In fact, in the West Indies, the price per pound of one species is more expensive than

A piece of a fossil stromatolite reef, unearthed in northern Ontario.

steak. Needless to say, it is now not very common. Most of these algae seem to prefer the areas of the reef that are in the waves, either on the reef top or on surf-torn beach rock areas.

The visible reef plants include the corallines, which either encrust or have calcium carbonate in the body, the tiny plant cells or zooxanthellae in the bodies of the corals, which assist in the depositing of calcium carbonate, the blue-green, green, brown and red algae, and finally the often extensive beds of turtle or eel grasses, which are not algae, and which grow surprisingly rapidly.

It is an impressive array indeed, and one which supports a great variety of herbivores. To be successful as a herbivore it is necessary to both eat or swallow the plant, and then digest it. Certain fishes may not have the correct digestive enzymes to be able to make use of the plants, and must therefore be swallowing the plants inadvertently as they feed on other things. Scientists still do not agree on whether certain species are true herbivores.

Crustaceans are an important group of herbivores. These creatures, such as the crabs, shrimps and lobsters, with stiff outer armour and jointed legs have no backbone. On a reef, crabs are usually hard to find because they often remain hidden in the daytime, and come out at night to feed. Most are not strict herbivores, and will augment their vegetarian diet with a wide variety of material that they find as they probe around in the sand and crevices with their little claws. One, which grows to a considerable size, is the grotesquely shaped spider crab, with enormous spoon-shaped tips on its claws. At night it sits in mats of algae, picking it up delicately in its overgrown "dessert spoons" and stuffing it into its mouth at an incredible rate.

Living in shells stolen from snails, hermit crabs often have to "trade up" to larger-sized shells as they grow.

Not all crabs hide during the day, but are so well camouflaged that they are almost impossible to see unless they move. The camouflage is often a sponge completely overgrowing the back of the crab. But one of the most impressive tricks is that of the hermit crab, which hides in the stolen shell of a snail. The crab soon grows so that its body is coiled into the snail shell, dragging the shell everywhere, so that it always has a perfectly shaped hideout into which it can retreat in a flash. However, as it is constantly outgrowing its home, the shell it is wearing eventually becomes less effective as protection, leaving the crab vulnerable to predators, so the hermit crab must search to find a new shell. The crab is very unprotected when it leaves the old shell to climb into a new one, and so goes through elaborate precautions, lining up the two shells to be exposed for a minimum amount of time during the switch. It is not unusual for one crab to attempt to steal a shell from another hermit crab.

The reef lobster is probably the best-known crustacean herbivore, but it will pick up animal scraps, if they are available. Because the lobster is a commercially valuable species, a considerable amount of research has been done on its life history. It begins as an egg fertilized during or shortly after the male and female lobsters copulate—a very awkward-looking event. After the eggs have developed for a while, the female carries them under her tail until the young hatch and are released into the water, where they remain as free-floating drifters for many months. Once settled to the bottom, they grow very quickly, and after just a few weeks have staked out a cave to use as a refuge in the daytime, coming out at night to feed on algae patches. By the age of three years, the reef lobster is quite a respectable size; its northern cousin requires nearly seven years to reach the same size.

Even more important among the spineless plant-eating creatures are the snails and sea slugs (nudibranchs). Because they have no "jaws," they can't take bites or chunks out of plants; instead they have a very rough tongue which is used to rasp or file off bits of algae. Despite their hard shell protection, snails are quickly eaten if movement betrays their presence, so they remain hidden in the daytime. Oddly enough, nudibranchs (meaning "naked gills"), which are really just snails that have lost their shells, are often out in the daytime, unprotected. Instead, they are remarkably well camouflaged. The most common Caribbean nudibranch has beautiful, frilled green and white coloured gills on its back, a pattern that blends so well into the background that few divers ever see them. Others are mottled shades of mauve, identical to the coralline and red algae among which they hide and feed. In deeper water, nudibranchs are often truly bizarre, varying from royal purple to electric yellow, or scarlet red and black. Most are small, less than a few centimetres in length, but one or two are moderately large, such as the sea hare, which reaches a length of twenty centimetres or more. Not particularly well camouflaged, the sea hare is a dull green streaked with tiny crooked black lines, but it does have a remarkable defense. If anything bites it, or even bumps hard against it, it spurts out a large cloud of bright purple ink—enough to discourage most predators.

Another important herbivore is the sea urchin, an animal that looks like a squashed tennis ball with spikes glued onto its body, but which is actually closely related to the starfish. The sea urchin skeleton which often washes up on beaches after storms reveals this relationship—the pattern clearly visible of the five "starfish" arms rolled up over the back with the mouth, centrally located, underneath the body. The mouth has a set of five very strong teeth that are used to chop off seaweed. In some species these teeth are so strong that they can be used to grind away at the calcium carbonate of both coral and coralline algae. The protective spikes or spines may be extremely long and sharp, as in the abundant black sea urchin (*Diadema*), or quite short and blunt. In slate pencil urchins the spines are fat, elongate pieces of what feel like stone. One large black Pacific sea urchin, fortunately not very common, has dangerously poisonous little devices hidden among the spines. In a normal sea urchin these little three-pronged pinchers are used to catch and hold bits of food and pass them to the mouth, but in this dangerous species, they are also armed with a poison.

There are many different species of sea urchins, some of which live in tight caves in the surge zone of the reef, others that live buried in the sand. They do not have true eyes, but are sensitive to light, so they can discern the approach of darkness, or even the passing of a shadow, and when darkness falls they move out of the caves and crevices to feed. A few species live in turtle grass where there are few

One trick used by "eolid" nudibranchs is to swallow coral polyps so that the nematocysts will grow into their skin. These walking dart guns advertise themselves boldly, warning off predators.

Cross-section of a chambered nautilus shell from the Indian Ocean. The heavy shell consists of many chambers, each containing a gas used for buoyancy so that the mollusc can swim freely on the deep edges of coral reefs.

caves to be found. They have the habit of placing bits of old leaves, shells and coral rubble on their upper surface. To a diver, these ludicrous little piles of debris do not seem to be much of a camouflage, so there may be another, as yet unexplained reason for the sea urchin's covering habit. *Diadema*, the black sea urchin, is also found feeding at night on turtle grass, but only if there is a patch reef nearby to which it can retreat in the day. Because the distance that a sea urchin can walk in a night is not very great, the patch reefs have a ring around them barren of grass, that is exactly the width that a sea urchin can walk and return in the course of a single night.

A most unlikely underwater customer, the excessively unattractive sea cucumber, is also a close relative of starfish, but looks like a grossly overgrown, wrinkled sausage. On the reef, they are often lightly sprinkled with sand and well hidden from the reef visitor, although a few are garish, and have a many-branched, brightly coloured organ called a tentacle, spreading from the mouth. The usual sea cucumber, however, is most often black, brown, or a subdued orange.

Their lugubriously slow-motion movements are deceptive; the animal creeps along the reef sand, sweeping the upper layer of sand particles and blue-green algae into its mouth. The sea cucumber's acid stomach works on the calcium carbonate sand, causing it to partially dissolve, while enzymes digest the algae. When the sea cucumber is finished digesting the algae, the sand it gets rid of is composed of finer particles. Recently, scientists have discovered that the skeletons of plants and animals have a protein glue holding the calcium carbonate particles together. It appears that the sea cucumber (and possibly anything else that eats coral rock) may be able to digest and gain benefit from the protein. These quiet little machines grinding away at the sand are so effective and abundant in some areas that they can pass the upper few centimetres of the entire sand layer of a lagoon through their stomachs three times every year, dramatically reducing the size of the sand grains in the lagoon.

Most sea cucumbers are short and fat, but a few nocturnal species are long, skinny, flaccid and very sticky to touch, because minute, glass, anchor-shaped spicules catch on your skin. In some areas of the tropics sea cucumbers are favoured as a food, but it is not wise to try them on your own, since many are poisonous to humans. Like other creatures that have no obvious defense, the sea cucumbers do have one "desperation" measure; if they are very roughly handled, they will spew out a great pile of the internal digestive tract. This white mass of spaghetti must be more attractive than the tough outer skin of the cucumber to the predator, which eats the innards in preference. Satisfied, the predator then leaves the cucumber to regrow its inner parts.

These unusual creatures have the mouth at one end and the cloaca (opening for disposal of both waste and reproductive products) at the other. Unlike most animals, which have the breathing apparatus associated with the head or mouth end, sea cucumbers breathe through the cloaca, drawing water into a set of gills inside the body.

The cloaca is therefore often open and relatively unguarded. The pearl fish has evolved to take advantage of this fact, and with its very long and slender tail aimed carefully at the opening, darts backwards right inside. The fish is remarkably big, often three-quarters as long as the whole sea cucumber. Most pearl fish are brown, black, or a bright coppery colour, and use the sea cucumber as a hideway during the daytime, sometimes nibbling on the inner organs of the poor creature. To preserve its home, however, it cannot eat so much that the life of the sea cucumber is endangered, so on night travels it forages for small crustaceans to supplement its cucumber diet.

Perhaps because the tropical regions have been stable for a longer time than the northern regions, or perhaps for a variety of as yet unknown reasons, many truly herbivorous fishes have evolved only in the tropical regions, a fact which may seem surprising when you consider that plants are not nearly as abundant on reefs as they are on the shores of most temperate continents. It may be that plants are not as abundant on reefs because fishes are eating them almost as fast as they grow. Experiments have shown that if the fishes are excluded from the reef by a fence, algae grow rapidly and threaten to overrun it. As soon as the fences are removed, fish move in in hordes to clean up the fresh algae.

There are also many more species of plants on coral reefs than there are in a comparable area on a northern shore. One puzzling result of excluding reef fishes is that the number of species in the rich new plant growth is very small, much smaller than the number that normally grow on a reef. Is it possible that there are fewer species in the north because of the lack of grazing fishes? Might it be that a predator reduces the ability of one species to dominate, thereby allowing others to find a way to make a living?

Whatever the reason for their existence, herbivorous fishes on a coral reef are prominent. In lagoons, schools of silvery brown, elongate fish called mullets also use the surface layers of the sand as a source of algae, possibly deriving some benefit from the protein matrix of the sand. When they take in sand through their triangular mouths, they seem to spit some of it out, and some falls out the gill covers. They are sorting the sand so it is just the right size to be ground up in an organ similar to a gizzard, and then digested in their long intestines (herbivorous fishes have longer intestines than their carnivorous cousins).

Another plant-eating fish is the sea chub, a fat-bodied fish that feeds on floating *Sargassum*, or attached plants. Small crabs and clams are also found in their stomachs, and it is not certain whether they are taking the animals by mistake. Because they spend some of their life in the open water, they are fast swimmers, and difficult to approach on a reef.

Combtooth blennies, so named because of their small, close-set flexible teeth, have a very special habitat; they are usually found in the surge channels and on the reef tops right in amongst the crashing waves, which means that at low tides they must be able to leap from pool to pool, and at times even make their way over wet coral and

One researcher found that when he killed the coral in a small section of a reef on the Pacific coast of Panama, the number of corals that took over was greater than the number that had been there previously; whereas when he did the same experiment on the Caribbean side the disturbed area was dominated at first by only a few species of coral. The questions of how different species divide up the resources, how species came to be different, and different in what numbers in each area continue to puzzle scientists.

While most sea cucumbers, relatives of the starfish, are commonly seen in the day-time, this species is noctur-nal, elongate, flaccid and sticky to the touch. They feed by sweeping into their mouths the upper layer of sand particles which have algae growing on them.

weeds. They scrape filamentous algae off the coral rocks, but at times consume animals as well. Most are very well camouflaged, but a few can be easily seen on the reef. In the Caribbean, for instance, the red-lip blenny is a cocky-looking inhabitant found from near the reef top ridge to depths of over fifteen metres. This fish is small (fifteen centimetres would be a giant), dark brown, or blotchy with bright red margins on the fins and lips, and rests on its fins as if they were stubby legs. It challenges most intruders by rushing out and threatening to bite them. Although they have flexible teeth in the front of the jaws for scraping algae off rocks, they also have a formidable set of recurved canines in the back of the mouth that can inflict a nasty wound if the would-be intruder presses his advantage. Relatives of the red-lip blenny from the Pacific sometimes have a venom associated with these rear fangs, that is not likely to be fatal, but can cause an ugly reaction.

Aggressiveness is not limited to blennies, however, and some of the most feisty are the damselfish. These perky little fish come in many different shapes and colours. Many of the bottom-loving damselfishes are herbivores. Most are also highly territorial, defending their home against surprisingly large species. Often damselfish will fly up to the attack one after another, inadvertently combining their efforts to ensure that the intruder is driven off. Divers have often been shocked to find a brilliant little blue-and-gold fish furiously biting at their legs or hands, or even vigorously attacking their face masks. These attacks are startling and amusing rather than dangerous to the divers, but to the damselfish, it is very serious.

Territory (any area defended by an animal) is an important facet in the lives of many reef creatures. The presence of food, and, often more important, good hiding places, a choice of night-resting spots, or a cave in which eggs can be hidden, are all reasons for defending a

Damselfish are often highly territorial and, despite their small size, species such as this cocoa damselfish will defend an area as large as two metres across — even attacking divers.

The surgeon fish is a voracious herbivore found on all coral reefs. Truly herbivorous fish are found primarily in tropical waters.

territory. In fact, on a coral reef, space and cover are the usual limiting factors, not food. Territorial fish that feed exclusively on bottom plants must defend a large enough area that the amount of food contained in it is sufficient, but not so big that it is a wasteful battle to defend the unnecessarily large horde. A number of damselfish have hit upon a technique for reducing the amount of territory: they have become farmers, carefully cultivating part of their chosen territory. In the Caribbean, the three-spot damselfish often chooses an area in thickets of staghorn. In the course of time, thread-like filaments of algae grow on the dead staghorn coral branches, but so do sponges, hydroids and numerous other things, which the damselfish carefully weeds out. The fish also picks off all would-be browsers like snails, nudibranchs, and crabs, then carries them to the edge of the territory and spits them out. Careful nibbling by the damselfish maintains the algae at the correct length for maximum rate of growth and ease of feeding and tending.

Another herbivore, the surgeon fish has taken to travelling in schools, so that by sheer weight of numbers it overwhelms the defending territory holder to eat up the stock of food. Surgeon fish earn their name from the weapon carried at the base of their tail—a scalpel-like blade that is used to slash at other fish. Some blades are as long as two centimetres and tipped with a poison. The fish are slab-slided and very high-bodied. Many are brilliantly coloured, perhaps advertising the formidable nature of their armament. Surgeon fish are especially common in shallow water where plants are most abundant. Excellent swimmers, they manage to move effortlessly in and out of the crashing surf, stopping with the surge to nibble at the algae, and then moving on again with the wave.

Huge chopping beaks and a grinding mill hidden in the throat characterize the parrotfish, impressive herbivores on the reef. The bumphead parrotfish reaches weights of hundreds of kilograms, and has a beak powerful enough to snap boulders. A procession of these mammoths moving down the reef can be awesome indeed. Other parrotfish are never larger than a few centimetres, but most weigh one to five kilograms. Parrotfish schools overwhelm damselfish territory holders, crunching patches of coralline algae, or chomping coral twigs. As algae and coral pass through the grinding mill and stomach, the fish digests out the nutritive materials and the rest is sent raining to the bottom. It is estimated that many species of parrotfish are capable of chopping, grinding, and digesting calcium carbonate from algae and corals at a rate of about a quarter of their body weight per day. About ninety kilograms of sand can be generated in a year by a small (one kilogram) parrotfish. One large bumphead parrotfish can literally create millions of grams of sand per year. Biting the tips off staghorn coral provides a site for algae; in a sense the parrotfish farm the algae even though they do not protect the territory. Parrotfish scrape coral polyps and the underlying skeleton off brain and boulder corals. Whether they do this as herbivores looking for zooxanthellae, or to get the animal tissue of the polyp is a moot question; perhaps they derive energy from both sources.

Contrary to many published accounts, surgeon fish cannot erect the spine using muscles (there are none to do it), and must rely on expertly arching the body to bare the blade as they swim past the intended victim.

A wide variety of creatures are first-level carnivores, feeding on herbivores. Carnivorous snails such as whelks, are probably the most important predator of other snails. Instead of using the tongue to rasp off bits of seaweed, they use it to drill holes through the shell and into the meaty part of the hapless herbivorous snail.

Impressive numbers of creatures are fond of crabs and sea urchins. One predator that specializes in feeding on crabs is the octopus, a strange creature related to the snails and clams, but possessing a very hard and sharp beak, jet propulsion, eight entangling arms and eyes that seem to see everything. Because they themselves are greedily snapped up by considerably larger fishes, they normally hide in darkened caves that have a pile of coral rubble at the entrance, with one mobile eye peeking out. At night they roam far from their caves, and with darting, feeling arms, catch unwary crabs. Their ability to alter their colour pattern with startling rapidity enhances the camouflage, but if attacked, they share with the sea hare, a distant relative, an ability to shoot out a thick black cloud of ink that hangs in the water, while the octopus jets off to safety.

Moray eels, those snake-shaped fish, gasping denizens of dark caves of the reef, are expert crab hunters, creeping through the darkness of night. One white-bodied moray eel in the Indian Ocean lives in water ankle-deep on the inner side of atoll reef tops, hiding carefully in undercut edges of rocky shorelines, waiting for scuttling crabs to dart into the water, after some morsel, or to escape from an

Moray eels, of which there are many species, some brightly coloured, spend the day mostly hidden in coral caves. The gaping jaws of this golden-tailed moray indicate a threat.

Flatfish, which have both eyes on one side of the head, are not common on coral reefs. This peacock flounder, however, lies in ambush on the sand, hidden by its shape and colour.

aerial predator. In less than a second, the eel strikes from the cave and crushes the crab. The moray, lashing its head back and forth, slithers back into hiding with the crab. A few morays are equipped with blunt teeth and enlarged jaw muscles for a powerful crushing bite, rather than sharp daggers. These are used for grinding shells of heavily armoured crabs, snails or clams.

Divers' fears of morays are only partly warranted, because most morays are not likely to jump out and bite. A few aggressive species grow to a very large size (in excess of 1.5 metres), and could cause grave injury or even death. In almost all situations, however, unless the diver is actively teasing the moray, they remain quietly in their caves. But sticking an arm or leg in a reef cave, poking at a large moray, or attempting to feed one from your hand is asking for trouble. Although a few divers have done all of those things and come away unscathed, those that tried it with an aggressive species, or even one that objected to sharing food with a hand, have scars to remind them of a painful experience. In one instance, a scientist who was collecting large morays to study the fish-poison ciguatera, shot at a moray, missed, and was startled to have the moray dive out of the cave right at him. Swimming rapidly back for the boat, he frantically attempted to shoo the very large and angry beast away. Suddenly, the moray lunged and ripped a huge slash in his arm just below the elbow. This is a very unusual event, but it illustrates the fact that a molested moray may attack.

At night or at dusk, when vision is a problem, it is easier to trespass into what the moray may feel is excessive rudeness. People who have been bitten by small morays say that it feels like toothed pliers gripping your flesh. A few have had the wit to remain calm and simply leave the hand or arm quietly in place until the moray senses the unfamiliar feel of soft, warm flesh, and lets go. Because the moray's teeth slant backwards into its throat, a sudden yank might free your hand or arm, but the moray's teeth would rip the flesh. If the yank was unsuccessful, the moray would simply anchor more securely in the cave, and morays are so strong that it is unlikely that you could pull free.

There are many weird fish in the ocean, but perhaps none so weird and yet commonplace as the fish that lies on its side with both eyes on one side of its head, one eye having wandered there from the other side of the head while the fish was young. Flounders or flatfishes, first-level carnivores, lie inconspicuously on sand or coral rubble, altering their body colour patterns to suit the sediment, waiting for unwary little crabs, fish or worms to wander by. Close up, many reef flatfishes have bright colours, but these colours usually seem to "disappear" when the fish is viewed against the natural background. They are usually small, unlike the giant northern flounders such as the halibut.

Lobsters and crabs (as well as a host of small damselfish and juveniles of other species) are the prey of snappers, grunts and

Snappers are one of many groups of carnivores which lurk on coral reefs, and are typified by having large jaws, heavy teeth, and broad, wedge-shaped tails which allow rapid acceleration.

This Caribbean spotted hind is one of many species of predatory groupers found on coral reefs, but it is unusual because it has several different colour phases, some bicoloured as above, some occasionally vivid red, or bright gold.

groupers, all of which are large-mouthed, medium-sized to enormous predators. Groupers or sea basses range in size from finger-length to nearly three metres long and five hundred kilograms, the largest of which, the jewfish, is capable of swallowing a diver whole. Barrel-shaped and slow-moving, the largest groupers are usually cave-dwellers in the daytime. When approached or molested, they are reluctant to leave the caves and will emit a threatening sound. Other groupers may spend most of their time either in the water column above the reef, or lurking among the corals, but the most important time of day for feeding is dawn and dusk, when the schooling fish are settling into or emerging from their nighttime hiding places.

During the day, snappers, emperors and grunts spend much of their time together in large groups or schools as a defense against predators, because while it makes the presence of the prey fish very obvious, the mass of confusion from crisscrossing and moving individuals within the school makes it impossible for a predator to find and follow one member. To further add to this defensive confusion, schoolers are often either bright and silvery, so that the sunlight glints off each member, making them hard to distinguish, or they have stripes and bars to break up the body outline. A mass of striped fish moving together makes it very hard to tell where one stripe begins and the next ends. Occasionally the predator simply slashes through the school with his mouth open and hopes for the best, and if a predator is big enough and the prey species small and closely packed, this technique can work. One scientist observed sharks to "herd" small fish into an extremely tight school and then to bite off chunks of the school.

But this is a very rare occurrence. It is far more efficient for a predator to take prey that are fairly large in relation to its own body size.

Prey in a school have the advantage of effectively having hundreds of pairs of eyes watching for danger, and they can manoeuvre faster than the predator whose random strike may well hit nothing but open water. Predatory strategy seems to be to move lazily about, waiting patiently for one of the members of the school to make a slight mistake, such as getting a little beyond the edge of the school, or turning the wrong way, so that its form can be picked out as going cross-grain. A sudden surge of power, and the predator catches the careless individual before it can hide back in the school. To watch such a strike is a sobering experience. Usually it is over, and the predator is busily chomping before you realize what has happened. The entire reef seems to dive for cover and then cautiously returns to normal activity.

Snappers, grunts and emperors leave their protective schools at dusk to hunt over the reef and lagoon grass flats for crustaceans. Grunts have an odd, and as yet not fully explained behaviour in schooling. The school will often remain near a patch reef during the daytime. A few of the dominant or larger fish in the group may defend a particular spot on that reef, perhaps one that is near an overhang. They never use it for food or reproduction, and if the school is threatened and moves away as a body, they move with it. On its return they resume territorial behaviour, an odd mix of two seemingly opposite behaviour patterns.

As grunts move along rush-hour routes at dusk towards the feeding grounds, they join a wary group of extraordinarily dopey-looking fish, the porgies, which are also carnivores. An extension of one of the bones below the eye gives them a down-at-the-mouth appearance. Porgies are not found on the shallow reefs very often, partly because they are so wary, but mostly because they specialize in hunting on grass flats and in the deeper areas of reefs.

Large front teeth characterize hogfishes and the extremely large humphead wrasses which are both active crustacean predators. Like the rest of the wrasses, they are constantly on the move, investigating crevices, peering in little holes, then rushing off down the reef, stopping quickly to snap at prey, then swooping off again.

Wrasses also exhibit dramatic changes in colour pattern and shape as they change from juveniles to adults. The common blue-head wrasse (a voracious scavenger, eating anything that moves if it is the right size) begins its juvenile life as a bright yellow fish with a large black dot on its dorsal fin. As it matures into adulthood, the fish takes on a barred, dusky-yellow colour, sometimes with a dark or diffuse stripe down its side. In this phase, males and females generally spawn in large groups, but in a remarkable change of gears, about four per cent of the adult females undergo a rapid sex change, becoming male, and acquiring a brilliant blue head separated from the rest of the body by a chalk white or green bar banded on its margins by wide bars of jet black. These "supermales" disdain the communal spawning events. Selecting an individual female, the supermale courts and spawns with

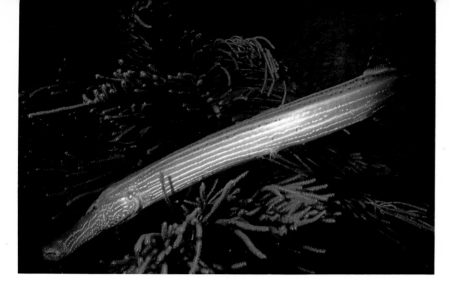

her alone. He may then rush off and court another female to spawn with her alone, but never joins in the crowd.

Intersexuality in fishes is surprisingly common. Many kinds of parrotfish also have a supermale or axillary male phase derived from females. In some species of damselfish, and anthiid basses, virtually all of the juveniles and most of the adults are females. Dominant males maintain large harems, and spawn with all of the smaller-sized females. If the male is eaten or dies, the largest female grows exceedingly rapidly, changes sex and becomes the dominant male in the harem. In some groupers, the fish are both sexes, and during spawning can switch from functioning as one sex to the other, sometimes more than once. It sounds very confusing, but the groupers obviously have it sorted out. The advantage to this type of arrangement is that no matter whom you meet, it is possible to spawn together, and in fish that tend to live relatively solitary lives, this could be crucial to survival.

Some grunts, snappers and porgies also eat sea urchins, even the very large-spined, black sea urchins, a diet that stains the inside of their mouths a deep purple from the colour of the spines oozing into the tissue after the spines have punctured their mouths. One fish that eats sea urchins, the triggerfish, has a special trick. By rolling on its side, it gets as close to the underside of the sea urchin as possible, then rapidly and repeatedly blows water under the urchin. With luck and skill the triggerfish can cause the sea urchin to roll over. The spines around the sea urchin's underparts are short and blunt, little protection from the sharp teeth of the triggerfish.

Some carnivores that feed on herbivores are perfectly happy to increase the size of their dinner by adding smaller animals that feed on herbivores. As well, a minor army of new lurking predators enters the picture at this point. Groupers, snappers, flatfish and a whole new regiment of moray eels (those with the big snaggly teeth, as opposed to those with the crab-and clam-crushers), lie in wait for the unwary damselfish or wrasse as it settles down for the night, or neglects to notice the grouper or snapper lurking in a crevice nearby. But in addition to the familiar forms there are some remarkable new ones.

The trumpetfish is so skinny that it resembles a piece of squashed but flexible water pipe, ending in a flattened tube with a little trap-door mouth. The trumpetfish hides in gorgonians, which its elongate form resembles, standing on its head and allowing itself to be washed back and forth in the surge, looking just like another piece of gorgonian. It slides stealthily through the water towards some busy damselfish or inquisitive wrasse, until, just the right distance away, the trumpetfish darts forward with amazing speed, and using a powerful suction created by the ingeniously designed slurp-gun mouth, literally inhales the damselfish.

Or consider a fish with a huge mouth, a flattened head, and no buoyancy organ, lying solidly on the bottom with thirteen venomous spines on its back, and a skin so apparently tattered, torn, and mottled in hue, that it is almost impossible to see in a weed patch. From this cover, with eyes upturned, the scorpionfish waits hidden for some unobservant fish of the right size to swim close enough to be caught with the charge and gulping inrush of water that marks the scorpionfish's lunge.

Poisonous spines seem an unnecessary embellishment, but scorpionfish are not large, less than thirty centimetres in length, so if discovered by a predator they would be exceptionally easy to catch. A threatened scorpionfish raises its dorsal spines in response and then clumps off down the reef. As it swims along in hops, the pectoral or side fins are turned over, exposing a brilliant pattern of contrasting dark and light spots, lines and circles to advertise its dangerous nature. If even this fails, and the scorpionfish is chased, it speeds up and expands the brightly coloured pectoral fins to their fullest. With a sudden spurt of speed it dives for the bottom, stirs up the sand to cover its action and darts off to the side, folding its pectoral fins back to their normal hidden position. The predator following along sees the flurry of sand, the disappearance of the pectoral fins and dives for the last spot it saw the scorpionfish. But the scorpionfish used the flurry of sand as a ruse; it is now nowhere near the spot the predator last saw it.

Lionfish, near relatives of the scorpionfish, take an exactly opposite philosophy. Bizarre, highly colourful and brazen, they advertise their presence with orange and black stripes, and a huge, frilly expanse of pectoral fin flouncing in the water. By spreading their pectoral fins and shivering them, they gradually and carefully "herd" prospective prey into a blind alley. Divers should approach these Indo-Pacific fish with caution. Spines in the fin on its back are very poisonous, and while only a small proportion of stings are fatal, they are all extremely painful. The lionfish is capable of driving its body in a rush, spines first, towards the offending diver.

Many first-level carnivores, and some herbivores, are intermediate in size. A few of the largest and most impressive predators are those that feed on the intermediate to moderately large fishes on the reef but are themselves virtually immune to predation, such as the barracuda, the largest groupers, moray eels, and the sharks. Their habits make them both first- and second- level carnivores, and at the same time, top predators in the community.

Barracuda are large, silvery, elongate fish that in some species form schools. The great barracuda is often reported to reach gargantuan sizes of three to four metres, but the largest specimen ever landed was only two metres long. They have large eyes, and a cruel, underslung lower jaw tapering to a sharp point armed with long, sharp and protruding teeth. Divers sometimes become aware of a sensation of being watched, and turn around to the heart-stopping sight of a large barracuda, jaws working slowly, drifting much too close and obviously looking them over. Fortunately, the number of authenticated cases of attacks on humans is very small indeed, and in most of those, the diver speared the fish first, or the barracuda mistakenly interpreted a shiny bit of clothing or jewellery to be an injured fish.

Barracuda are specialists in preying on schooling fishes, getting within striking distance of about two body lengths. A barracuda can cover the three to four metres in a fraction of a second because of its great broad wedge tail that allows the fish to move a large amount of water and, with a single, powerful swipe of the tail, accelerate to nearly full speed. Such a lunge can only be sustained for a short period of time, which is why the striking distance is a function of the body length. When striking large prey, the barracuda often cuts it in half, swallowing one half first, then lazily turning around catches the second half before it hits the bottom.

Sharks, infamous killers of the sea, have become a popular subject for motion picture and television screens. Almost any species of shark found on a reef, even quite a small one, is capable of inflicting serious or fatal injury to a swimmer. Because they routinely eat their prey in chunks, rather than swallowing it whole as most of the reef predators do, they are a real threat even to large creatures. Sharks inhabiting reefs can be divided into two types: sluggish sharks that lie on the bottom; and the fast, free-swimming forms. The largest of the bottom sharks are the nurse sharks which frequently reach lengths in excess of four metres, have only tiny jaw teeth, and are not aggressive but can be curious. The near presence of a black animal nearly as big as an automobile, staring at you with small, intense eyes, is enough to give one pause. The intellectual knowledge that they are not aggressive is a bit of information you hope the shark shares. A lack of aggressiveness and tiny teeth do not mean they are incapable of catching fish and ripping chunks of flesh off them; they are nocturnal predators, that have highly sensitive, whisker-like barbels to help them detect prey in the dark.

Free-swimming reef sharks, or requiem sharks, are more common on reefs close to open-water environments, such as atolls. Although fairly small, averaging one to three metres, the sharks are active, cruising over large ranges of the reef, and hunting for prey mainly in the late afternoon, and early darkness. Offshore sharks, often larger, sometimes enter the reef environment, prowling the shallow waters through the darkest hours of the night, after which they return to deep water. The most common food items for the reef sharks are grunts, snappers, parrot- and surgeon fishes, and sometimes squid. Because

Many species of scorpionfish have skin that appears ragged and multicoloured, resembling the patches of seaweed and coral in which they lie hidden in ambush, waiting for unsuspecting prey to swim by.

sharks are large, their striking distance is also large. Motion pictures taken of a Pacific grey-reef shark attacking the propeller of a research submersible showed the beast striking from a distance of approximately four metres, and biting the propellor twice, all in the space of about half a second.

In the reef food web that begins with large aquatic plants, there is a progression of herbivores and two levels of carnivores, one feeding on herbivores, the second on other carnivores. Many creatures do not fit neatly, so must be considered omnivores. Creatures as different as nudibranchs and parrotfish fit into the same ecological place in the food chain, even though they have completely different ways of going about the business of being a herbivore. Single groups of fish often have more than one type of habit, like moray eels, some of which have blunt teeth for crushing clams and crabs, whereas others have long slender

teeth for catching swift and slippery fish. All of this fits together in a series of interwoven food chains. The term "food web" is applied to the mix of all the various chains. Some animals may participate in more than one of the chains, or at more than one level within it. This food web describes only a part of the whole reef community and accounts for only a fraction of the productivity and richness of the reef.

Also in the scorpionfish family, several species of lionfish in the Indo-Pacific advertise rather than camouflage their presence, warning would-be predators of their venomous dorsal spines.

Chapter Four

From Drifter to Detritus

Although complicated, the reef food web beginning with aquatic plants nevertheless leaves some unexplained questions, and experienced reef visitors will notice glaring omissions. No mention was made of sponges, coral polyps, or the myriad of small schooling fishes. Where do the worms, clams, starfish, angelfish, and butterflyfish fit in? Most of these are not a part of the food web that begins with large algae growing attached to the reef. They belong to a second food web which begins in the open ocean, many kilometres offshore, on a scale much too small to see with the naked eye.

Biological riches depend on the presence of nutrients, which in the open ocean are usually in short supply because they come from the land, the result of fertile, fresh-water river runoff into the sea. Inshore waters around the continents are filled with the suspended materials from the runoff. Further offshore, the water is saltier and clearer, and far offshore the water is extremely clear, implying that the material from the land has somehow disappeared from the water. In fact only the particulate matter has settled, forming bottom sediments around continents. Nutrients from this material have been leached and dissolved into the water.

Compared to offshore water, near-shore water is green in colour, the result of high concentrations of chlorophyll which are contained in the very large population of tiny green plant cells that are growing rapidly in response to the rich nutrient source near the shore. These are single-celled plants capable of breathing, carrying out photosynthesis and reproducing.

Abundant among these plants are diatoms, the most diverse of all algae. Shaped like minute pill boxes, the cell walls are impregnated with silica. Diatoms can be found in a wild array of shapes, most of which are devices to slow the sinking rate. They are not capable of moving against the currents, but move up and down in the water column.

Diatoms are members of the open-water, drifting world of microscopic plants and animals, the plankton. They are the single most abundant form of plankton of any kind, animal or plant, but they are not the only kind of plant plankton. The next most abundant, and possibly more important from an ecological point of view, are single-celled dinoflagellates, girdled by a small whip or flagellum that beats continuously, and a second whip that extends from the bottom of the cell, causing it to spiral in the water. These plants are common in tropical seas, and because of the very rapid life cycle, which may be complete in a few hours, they can create an amazingly large amount of plant tissue. These are the same type of cells that become zooxanthellae in corals.

"Red tides" develop in coral reef lagoons when the number of dinoflagellates gets extremely high, so concentrated that the water may be discoloured from the pigments in their cells. If the numbers are great enough the little plant cells may start to die off, and as they rot, their decay uses up all the oxygen in the water, causing other forms of life to die. The dinoflagellates also contain a poisonous substance which may kill fish. The magnificent "phosphorescence" (more properly, living light or bioluminescence) so characteristic of the tropical seas at night is mostly due to dinoflagellates. What a strange group of plants; symbiotic assistants of corals, free-living plankton, deadly poisonous enemies of fish and people, and yet creators of beauty in tropical night waters.

There are also microscopic animals in the water. Some are composed of single cells, larger than the planktonic plants, but still so small that it is difficult to see them without the aid of a microscope. Other multi-cellular planktonic animals are large enough to see easily without a lens. Through the microscope, a truly wonderful variety of exquisite creatures, varying from gossamer veils of siphonophores to fairy shrimp, populate the sea. Some are hyperactive, others delicate and slow, but always bustling through this crowd are the incredibly abundant copepods, pear-shaped creatures vaguely resembling shrimp. Most copepods are three or four millimetres long when fully grown, and swim through the water using a large pair of antennae which extend from the head, or using swimming legs located in the middle of their bodies. Many of the copepods are herbivores. They automatically filter plant cells, using the water turbulence created by swimming movements to bring food particles to the mouth, where they are strained out by a set of tiny bristles.

A similar creature, the juvenile barnacle, has a different arrangement of limbs, a shield-shaped skeleton and scoots through the water with a speed almost equal to the energetic copepods. Barnacles are related to shrimps and crabs, not clams, as their adult appearance might suggest. Juvenile crabs, shaped like minute shrimp wearing spiked helmets, cruise sedately through the water collecting plant cells.

Two remarkably abundant forms of "animals" (in the sense that they do not have chlorophyll in the cells) are single celled. Both Foraminifera and Radiolaria have the ability to send out an ooze of their vital body material and entangle little plant cells. Over geological time, the staggering numbers that have lived and died is partially recorded in the sediments, where their skeletons have collected. Much of the bottom ooze of the ocean which can be hundreds of metres thick is actually composed of the skeletons of these minute creatures. Together with the three groups of little crustaceans, the copepods, juvenile barnacles and juvenile crabs, they comprise most of the herbivores in the open-ocean food chain, which is based on dinoflagellates and diatoms as primary producers.

Just as on the reef, the food chains in the open ocean do not stop at the level of herbivore. A host of minute carnivores, ready to gobble up the small herbivores, include carnivorous copepods, but also other crustaceans such as mysids which look like many-legged shrimp.

There are too many different kinds of carnivorous, planktonic creatures to catalogue, but the more prominent include tiny bristle worms with little paddles on their sides, arrow worms, a unique group of nearly transparent, slender or arrow-shaped worms armed with a mouthful of curved spines for seizing prey, and a host of jellyfish relatives, most of them armed with nematocysts like the corals and gorgonians.

Ctenophores or comb jellies are one of the most beautiful plankton. They have rows of tiny bristles that beat continuously, creating a miraculous flickering play of rainbow colours (birefringence) down their transparent or pastel-hued sides. A pair of nematocyst-armed tentacles gather prey.

Unexpected animals have become planktonic. Near relatives of the snails have become diminutive and arranged the foot to function like a pair of tiny wings; one of the sea cucumbers, normally sedentary and lethargic, has spread a veil to parachute through the water in ultra slow-motion. The larvacean, a relative of the sedentary sea squirts, builds and then rests in a clear, barrel house, pumping a constant flow of water through it, drawing plant or animal plankton into a complex net. When sufficient plankton has been gathered, the larvacean eats the net and all its contents.

This is a food web that begins in the open ocean, and for the most part ends there, unless the ocean currents happen to flow past a coral reef, carrying with them their host of larval creatures and planktonic animals and plants. As the open-ocean microcosm approaches the reef, it faces a virtual wall of mouths composed of coral reef animals.

Perhaps the most obvious plankton catcher is the animal that makes up most of the reef, coral. At night, when so many creatures in the sea come out of hiding, the corals open up, their nematocyst-armed tentacles waiting under the cover of darkness until little crustaceans or worms brush by. The coral's barbed arrows and lassos pierce and

OPPOSITE: *Of the many types of shrimp that live on coral reefs one of the most common is the pistol shrimp, so named for the claw which, instead of pinching, is shaped like a hammer and anvil to make a loud snapping sound. Often these shrimp are so common that the coral reef is far from being a "silent world."*

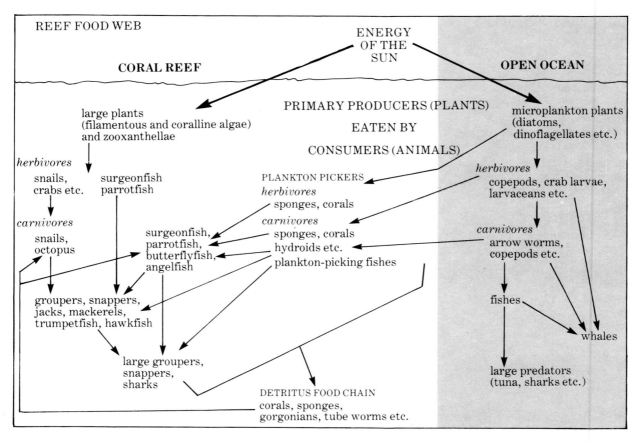

REEF FOOD WEB

CORAL REEF

ENERGY
OF THE
SUN

OPEN OCEAN

PRIMARY PRODUCERS (PLANTS)

EATEN BY

CONSUMERS (ANIMALS)

large plants
(filamentous and coralline algae)
and zooxanthellae

microplankton plants
(diatoms,
dinoflagellates etc.)

herbivores
snails,
crabs etc.

surgeonfish
parrotfish

PLANKTON PICKERS
herbivores
sponges, corals

herbivores
copepods, crab larvae,
larvaceans etc.

carnivores
snails,
octopus

surgeonfish,
parrotfish,
butterflyfish,
angelfish

carnivores
sponges, corals
hydroids etc.
plankton-picking fishes

carnivores
arrow worms,
copepods etc.

groupers, snappers,
jacks, mackerels,
trumpetfish, hawkfish

fishes

large groupers,
snappers,
sharks

whales

DETRITUS FOOD CHAIN
corals, sponges,
gorgonians, tube worms etc.

large predators
(tuna, sharks etc.)

trap the small creatures, arms draw it close to be pierced again and again until the struggling stops. The prey is drawn to a central area or rolled into the valleys of a brain coral where it is engulfed and digested. Some corals have large tentacles, others short; each is designed to catch different sizes of food. Some corals have tentacles so small that they really are not useful for catching live prey, but are designed to catch organic debris floating in the water. Because living coral forms an almost continuous sheet in many parts of the reef, most of the passing water currents are swept by coral tentacles.

The growth form of corals and gorgonians seems to depend in part on the needs of the zooxanthellae. Most leaf-like corals have expanded to allow a maximum amount of light to strike their surfaces. Even the branching forms resemble trees reaching for light. It happens that some of the adaptation for catching light is similar to that for increasing the amount of water that can be filtered to capture plankton.

Reaching up above the corals, and open at any time, gorgonians and sea fans flex arms up, reaching to get a first chance at passing plankton. Another coral relative, the sea anemone, can catch very large plankton or even a fish that is unlucky enough to bumble into the anemone's nematocyst-studded, dangerous arms. One small group of fish and shrimp, however, benefit from living in close physical contact

Small, fern-shaped colonial hydroids, relatives of corals and anemones, are commonly found in coral caves and crevices, and are early colonizers on new surfaces underwater, such as wharves and wrecks.

with the deadly tentacles. The anemonefish, a type of damselfish, is apparently immune to the anemone's stings that easily kill other fish. A healthy anemonefish is covered with a thick mucus coat that inhibits the nematocysts in the anemone's tentacles from firing. The fish wriggle and push their bodies right down into the anemone's tentacles, as if they were snuggling into a cosy wrap. In return for the protection the anemone affords, the fish will occasionally feed it scraps of food. Whether this is an important benefit to the anemone is unknown — perhaps the little fish is getting a free ride. Small, often partly transparent shrimp with startling patches of colour on the outside, hide in anemones as well. Many of these shrimp are very noisy, having a claw modified to operate like a hammer, rather than as a pincher. Their numbers are so great on a reef that they can easily be heard by swimmers.

Some species of tiny fishes have the ability to rest right on the live polyps of both corals and gorgonians, without being stung by nematocysts. Coral polyp-sitters use the same defensive mechanism as anemonefish — a thick coat of mucus. Most of the species that do this belong to a single family of extremely tiny fishes, the gobies.

Hydroids, near relatives of fire coral, hide in the caves and crevices waiting for the water currents or nighttime darkness to bring plankton within firing range of their powerful nematocysts. Hydroids are similar to small seaweeds in appearance, and are often among the first creatures to colonize new surfaces, such as on wrecks. Almost all big ones are found in deep water or far back in the recesses of coral caves, fortunately for the diver, because they can sting with a real wallop.

While corals wait passively for plankton to drift by and bumble into their waiting arms, the apparently less active sponges pump water through their bodies, sucking plankton into them, where it is filtered. The volume of water that a sponge pumps can reach several times its own volume per minute. Within the sponges, there are some that take both large and small plankton, having large pores, and other specialists that take only the small plankton through tiny pores. A few of the anemones have capitalized on the sponges' ability to suck water, and hide in the pores of the sponge, spreading their arms out to

The smallest known living animal with a backbone belongs in the group of fishes known as gobies. An Indian Ocean fish, it is one of nearly a thousand species of gobies, only a few of which grow to more than three or four centimetres in length. The smallest one matures at a length of eight millimetres, or about the width of your baby fingernail.

The tentacles of anemones are armed with powerful stinging cells, used to collect prey as large as a small fish. Clownfish, however, enjoy a rare immunity to the stings because of a thick mucous coat on their skin, and they can hide from their predators in the dangerous tentacles.

OPPOSITE: *Several families of shrimp are also able to hide in the anemone's stinging tentacles, although the mechanism for their immunity to the stings is not fully understood.*

intercept the plankton as it is wafted by on its way into the sponge.

The variety of shapes that sponges take is almost beyond classification. Some are round blobs, some are thin sheets spread over another surface, others reach up several metres with long, twisted pipes. The surfaces of sponges range from slick and slippery to rough and positively tattered. They live in deep and shallow waters, in the open, in caves and overgrowing the skeletons of other creatures such as corals and gorgonians. Shallow-water sponges are usually shades of grey-green or brown, but in deeper water, for some inexplicable reason, the sponges are red or bright purple, brilliant green or orange.

Sponges are not alone in having invented a water-pumping system for straining plankton. Clams, also seemingly inactive, are capable of generating a considerable current of water. Unlike sponges which have small intake and large exhaust pores, clams have one intake and one exhaust pore, each approximately the same size, although usually different in shape. Their water pump is a series of tiny hairs on the "gills" beating in one direction, carrying water over a series of fine grids and sticky tissues, which sieve and catch the plankton. Most clams, scallops and mussels on a reef are well hidden, tucked into crevices, or attached to the side of a gorgonian and looking like nothing but a lump. Many small species hide in the sand, sticking a little "snorkel" tube or siphon out of the sand to draw water down, but the number of individuals in each species is never very abundant.

A few species of clams are quite large, such as the pen shells, which lie buried upright in the sand. The shell is not heavy, but can reach thirty to fifty centimetres in length. Undisputed giants of the clam domain, and prominent members of the Indo-Pacific reefs (although never found in the Atlantic) are the giant killer clams. Legends about these enormous clams catching native pearl divers may not be incorrect. The shell itself can reach well over a metre in length

The largest clams found on coral reefs grow to over a metre in length. Their name "killer clam" comes from stories of native divers being trapped by them.

While it is possible giant "killer-clams" may have been responsible, it is more likely the skin-diving pearl divers drowned by reason of poor knowledge of their own physiology. By hyperventilating at the surface before they descended, they stay down longer than their bodies can stand the strain, and they faint, or become unconscious before attempting to return to the surface (a problem that modern, skilful skin-divers occasionally encounter).

and weigh upwards of one hundred kilograms. Like any clam, they close up when something touches the soft tissue, and it is conceivable that a careless diver might poke a foot or hand into the shell, only to have the valves of the shell close tightly and hold him long enough to cause him to run out of breath, thereby drowning. There would be no way to swim back to the surface carrying that weight, even if it were free of the bottom, which most of them are not, having become wedged into place over years of growth. On the other hand the giant clams usually close up much too quickly for a diver to be able to get a hand or foot between the valves before they close.

These giant clams can grow to an enormous size because like the corals, they enjoy a symbiotic relationship with tiny plant cells in their tissues, which allows them to secrete calcium carbonate very quickly. Unlike other clams, killer clams lie with their valves wide open, and spread an extensive curtain of flesh or mantle across the opening parallel to the ocean's surface, so that the zooxanthellae catch the maximum amount of sunlight.

It is one of nature's unexplained wonders that colours in animals like these are so prominent and varied. The mantles of killer clams can only be described as garishly beautiful, varying in hue from brilliant green or yellow to deep blues and purples, often streaked with electric shades of a markedly contrasting colour. The flesh of the clam is delicious, and is often used both as food for human consumption and bait for fishing, but occasionally this clam can cause paralytic shellfish poisoning. In Australia, the largest species is considered endangered, so it is against the law to kill them. Not all of the killer clams are big; many are no bigger than a child's hand, growing in tiny crevices, with only the brilliant hues of the mantle betraying their presence. All killer clams are found in shallow water, where the zooxanthellae can catch the light most easily.

The feather-star or crinoid is one of the sedentary and hidden creatures that catch plankton. Most often all that is visible of these creatures are a few slender stalks tentatively poking out of little crevices between coral boulders. Unlike a feather, however, the little branches can move and actively catch planktonic creatures as they go by. On rare occasions, divers may see the entire feather-star swimming with a graceful but somehow frantic motion of the arms, which come from a central body where the mouth is located. Because the arms are sticky to the touch, it is very easy to damage crinoids, their arms breaking off with the least strain.

Basketstarfish have a similar shape to crinoids but act quite differently. Thick branches come from a central body and immediately begin to split into twos, their branches subsequently also branching by twos, until a confused mass of tiny tendrils forms a circle around the core. During the daytime the basketstar finds a gorgonian or some other resting place, usually high off the bottom, and coils all its arms and tendrils around its central core and the gorgonian, becoming a shapeless mass on the stem. At night the star uncoils slowly, and using a few of its tendrils as an anchor, unfurls each arm completely. The multiple branches form a circular pattern, tiny tendrils filling the central part of the circle to form a net-like woven basket. Each of the tips seems to be in constant motion, grasping for the small planktonic creatures to carry them to the mouth at the central part of the circle.

One of the most beautiful, but also least conspicuous of fixed plankton catchers is the ascidian. Like paired, tiny, transparent bottles with gossamer nets ingeniously trapped in them, they pump water in one hole and out another, passing it through the minute nets, filtering out plankton. They are most often found in colonies in deep water, like little bottles strung on a line, or jumbled together on the bottom.

Recently scientists have discovered that there are reef plankton that somehow remain residents of the reef rather than just floating in from the open ocean. These tiny copepods and mysids actively swim into the lee of corals in invisible little schools, probably to feed on offshore plankton swept in. Some gather the tiniest plant cells drifting by, but others seem to be carnivores, feeding on the plankton animals. In these "plankton" schools, most of which are found in the lagoon areas where the currents are not so strong, the numbers of creatures can reach into the millions per cubic metre. At times they are so thick that the water has a blue-grey cast. Mysids are individually large enough to be seen easily by a diver, who usually mistakes them for larval fish. At the approach of a potential predator, mysid schools may move into caves or near coral boulders in the central part of a damselfish's territory. The damselfish rushes out to chase off the intruder, protecting its territory, and at the same time inadvertently protecting the school of mysids.

If sedentary plankton pickers reach out with branches to sample the water, trying to gain an advantage on the forms that cannot, then there must be a greater advantage to swim even further than the reaching tendrils to intercept the plankton before the corals, sponges and others have had a chance to filter the water. There are, however,

Taking advantage of the plankton-filled water being sucked in by the red, coral-boring sponge, tiny anemones live in its pores to intercept large plankton before the sponge can get it.

OPPOSITE: *Although there are few species of feather stars, or crinoids, in the Caribbean, the Indo-Pacific has many different forms of these sedentary, plankton-picking animals, such as the shallow-water species shown here.*

drawbacks to this idea. Creatures large enough to swim away from the reaching gorgonian and sponge branches, yet small enough to feed on plankton, are exactly bite size for many predators moving slowly over the reef. To avoid this, some relatively small fish such as the damselfish and fairy basslet move just a little way up off the reef, and then duck down into a cave as a predator approaches. Even this, however, has required the evolution of a special mouth—one that shoots out to form a suction tube so that plankton can be slurped up one by one. Some fish will leave the immediate reef area in schools, where, hidden in the confusion, each individual fish can feed on plankton until a predator approaches. Over and in front of reefs there are literally clouds of plankton-feeding fishes, sometimes so thick that they measurably reduce the amount of light reaching the reef. There is no doubt that plankton-feeding fishes intercept a significant proportion of the plankton before it reaches the corals and gorgonians waiting with outstretched arms and mouths.

Since swimming speed is a function of body size, the biggest plankton pickers will swim the farthest away from the coral. Body shape, however, is also a factor in speed. Larger fish with torpedo-shaped bodies and highly forked tails are the most adept interceptors of oncoming plankton, as well as the best at avoiding being eaten by the host of waiting predators. The bonnetmouths, found in all tropical oceans, are very elongate, with scissor-like tails and a mouth that shoots out to form a surprisingly long tube. They are rarely seen by divers because they are so swift, and can swim far off the reef. The similarly shaped fusiliers, although not present in the Atlantic, are very common elsewhere, seeming to stream in sheets over the reef. Most fusiliers have longitudinal stripes and are shades of blue, yellow, red or purple. Boaters near reefs often see them feeding close to the surface, their bright colours flashing as they dive and turn, chasing plankton. Mixtures of damselfish species create layers of plankton-eating fish below the fusiliers. In the Atlantic, the creole fish, a wrasse, has lost the typically large mouth and heavy front teeth

Schools of small fish pick plankton from the ocean currents as they drift over the coral reef. These damselfish are characterized by torpedo-shaped bodies, forked tails, large eyes and a mouth which can shoot out into the form of a tube to suck in individual plankton.

of wrasses, trading it for a plankton feeder's mouth. These fish can form immense schools a hundred metres across and kilometres in length. Atlantic creole fish act and look much like Indo-Pacific fusiliers.

Some species, such as reef herrings, anchovies and silversides, do not feed in the daytime, and leave the protection of their schools at dusk to move into open lagoon waters and to the outer face of the reef, feeding on plankton under the cover of darkness. They join another host of fishes that during the day were hidden in reef caves, including sweepers—the coppery, huge-eyed fish with a dramatic sweep to the belly, familiar to any diver who has peered into a cave during the day —and the large, bright-red cave-dwelling squirrelfish. At dusk, in the channels of the reef, it seems as if there could not possibly have been enough caves to contain all the squirrelfish that go by. Much smaller but also often red, the cardinalfish are nighttime feeders, some spending the day in caves, others in dense schools near the coral.

One of the most unusual plankton pickers avoids predators by living in burrows. Garden eels are pencil-thin, thirty to fifty centimetres long and live in small burrows on the open sand of lagoons, or in passes through the reef, where a constant sweep of current brings them fresh ocean waters. They live colonially, sometimes in huge numbers, and as they rise up, keeping their tails in the burrow, they resemble a garden of some exotic plant, swaying gently with the push and pull of the surge. Their tiny mouths are set at an oblique angle, making it easier to catch passing plankton. As a predator approaches, the eels sink slowly into the ground, until the entire field of swaying eels is gone. This behaviour makes them extremely difficult to study, and little was known about them until one scientist thought of setting up an underwater equivalent of the duck blind. From the cover of this tent she was able to observe them feeding, arguing, courting and mating.

In addition to open-ocean and schooling reef "plankton" there is a

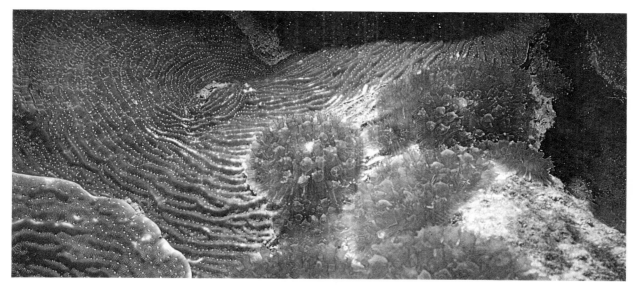

whole range of microscopic non-schooling plankton such as worms and crustaceans that can be found near the ocean bottom. Similar to open-ocean plankton, many have minor adaptations that enable them to hide in the sand or in caves, to crawl on surfaces, and to be camouflaged against the sediments. Like reef plankton, they can feed on both microscopic plants and animals.

A host of small fish hop, swim or skitter about, busily eating these near-bottom plankton. Many different species of these tiny fish can be found, indicating both an abundant food supply and a wide variety of habitats. Most of the species are gobies, often nearly transparent, moving around on fins used like tiny transparent legs. Very large eyes, and an impressive set of teeth help them catch small prey. Some are brightly coloured and hide in mats of plants or live in tiny caves. One goby lives in a sand burrow constructed by a small, blind shrimp working like a minute bulldozer rumbling up and down the tunnel, excavating sand and constantly repairing the walls if they should start to settle. The little goby sits placidly by the entrance to the tunnel, occasionally popping forward to catch passing plankton. While the shrimp is digging out the tunnel, he places one tip of an antenna on the body of the goby, continuously monitoring the little fish's position and activities. The goby, sighting approaching danger, dives into the tunnel, followed closely by the shrimp, which has been alerted by his antenna.

Fiercely territorial clinids, defending an area many times their own body size, and using the several rows of teeth on the jaws and in the roof of the mouth as weapons, are among the most formidable of the cigarette-sized predators. The most obvious clinids move about in the daytime in shallow water, busily chasing, popping sideways or forwards, to snatch near-bottom plankton. Less conspicuous is the tiny, spiny-headed clinid, which spends the day with about half of its body poking out of a minute, tubular cave, eyes peering anxiously around, ready to dart out and grab plankton, or retreat in a flash back

Both types of animals shown here are filter feeders. The lettuce coral has very tiny polyps which gather detritus, and the tunicates, or sea squirts, catch living plankton by pumping water through a net in their bodies.

into the little tube. The pike blennies, near relatives of the spiny heads, but with a duck-shaped beak, are also tube dwellers and have grown to a slightly larger size, perhaps ten centimetres in length. A fierce disposition and an enormously expanded, brightly coloured dorsal fin are used in frequent combat. Instead of actually biting, the belligerent little beasts merely threaten, attempting to impress each other with a larger or brighter dorsal fin. Often their arguments are over the ownership of the little tubes in which they make their homes.

The arrow clinid must surely be one of the most intriguing of the group. No more than five centimetres in length, this fish's head tapers to a point, and its body is slender. It hovers ready to attack, with the tail coiled back like a little spring, and when something comes within range, the coiled spring tail whips the little fish forward in a blinding burst of speed.

With a suction cup on its belly, the clingfish has been able to find its way into unusual and inaccessible habitats on reefs. Clingfish are one of the few species that can remain stationary in shallow, wave-swept areas where the suction cup helps them hold on as the waves sweep overhead. Other fish do not resist the motion of the waves, but move with it. To help them hold their positions, the clingfish have flattened heads that act something like the "spoiler" fins used on race cars to keep them pressed down on the ground as they go around corners. Not all clingfish live in wave-swept areas; a few live in the fronds of animals like gorgonians or crinoids. These clingfish are very small indeed, and have slender or tubular, rather than flattened heads. All of them are plankton predators.

It may seem unbelievable that a small fish can swim into the gaping and tooth-studded jaws of a large grouper, nonchalantly picking at the teeth, wandering down the predator's throat, and finally appearing through the gill covers, while the grouper's huge jaws are held politely apart, but it is a common occurrence. Beautifully striped shrimp will use their little claws to nip gently at the eyes or skin of a moray eel, or wander into the gasping, working jaws. How do they get away with it, and why do some of the big fish seem to hold themselves in incredibly awkward positions, heads down in the water, or on their sides, seeming to invite these little creatures to climb around in their mouths and on their bodies? The small fish and shrimp are cleaning diseased tissues from sores or are removing parasites that have clung to the sides, gills or mouth of the larger fish. Lacking fingers, the large fish cannot remove the parasites themselves, so they present the afflicted area of their bodies to the little fish that obligingly remove the offending parasites. In return for these favours, large fish grant immunity to the cleaners. Even if the larger fish is startled and must leave in a hurry, it will almost always take the time to cough the little fish or shrimp out of its mouth before leaving, rather than swallow it.

Cleaners are always considerably smaller than the fish they are cleaning, and therefore present no threat to them. It might be difficult to imagine how such a tenuous truce could develop. Probably the difference in size is partly responsible. Parasite-picking fish are related to fish that nibble at just about anything small and moving.

Possibly eons ago the small fish inadvertently began to pick at a small moving creature that it perceived to be moving around on a "large object," and did not at first interpret the large object as a fish. The larger fish would either not have noticed, or not have objected to having an annoyance removed by such a non-threatening process. In time, the relationship has developed into one clearly advantageous to both parties: the little fish no longer have to risk swimming high into the water column to feed on plankton, and engage in a type of "treaty" with potential predators.

This relationship has become so advanced that often cleaner fishes or shrimp will perform a little dance. A fish, seeing the dancer, lies down on the bottom, whereupon the shrimp prances out looking for parasites. The barber-pole shrimps, with their very long, white antennae, advertise only by appearance, and in fact for the most part do not clean fish in the daytime, only at night, specializing in morays.

In the Atlantic, the cleaner fish system works relatively well, although it has been shown that the larger fish will occasionally "make a mistake" and swallow a cleaner. In the Pacific, however, the situation has become a little complicated. A small number of a sneaky species of blenny have copied nearly exactly the colour pattern and shape of the cleaners. They even pull off a very convincing cleaner dance. On the other hand they tend to be a little bigger. Having fooled

In most coral reefs, a curious and mutually beneficial relationship occurs between large predatory fish and small "cleaner" fish. The small fish are allowed to wander into the gaping mouths and gills, and over the skin of the larger fish to remove diseased tissue or parasites.

the customer into thinking it will get a nice gentle cleaning, the con artist rushes up, unsheathes a huge pair of fangs (the teeth are so large that they must be housed in separate grooves in the skull, because they stick right up from the lower jaw, higher than the eyes), dives in and chops off a big hunk of fin or chunk of flesh from the unsuspecting customer. These sabre-tooth blennies will bite divers as well, a startling experience if you are not expecting it. Such predatory mimicry works only if the mimics and their bites are relatively uncommon, so that the prey do not have a chance to learn that there is a "cleaner" fish which bites. If the mimics were common, their bites would eventually discourage fish from using the cleaners, and the whole relationship would break down.

Some experiments have shown that if all of the cleaner shrimp and fishes are removed from an area, there may be a considerable decline in the health of the locally resident fish. As the cleaners return, so does the health of the population; sores and external parasites disappear again. Not all experimenters were able to find this result, so some areas are not as dependent on the relationship as others. A few parasites (relatives of the garden sow bug) have found a way to avoid being eaten by the cleaners by becoming exceptionally large, so large they can be seen on the heads of the fish as lumps half as big as the head.

With all of this activity a goodly amount of garbage is generated on a coral reef, partially the result of the death of minute organisms which drift as a gentle rain to the bottom. In addition to this, all animals must eliminate waste products. Some of it is carried away by water currents, but as much as possible is recycled, to extract the maximum amount of stored energy. Garbage, or organic debris, generated from all of these sources, has a polite scientific name — detritus, and it is the basis of still another food web.

Detritus is generated either up in the water column, from where it falls, or at the bottom, where it sits or rolls gently along. Detritus in the water column is, like plankton, gathered and filtered by many of the same sponges and clams.

Since elaborate mechanisms used to capture struggling animals are not necessary for gathering detritus, few of the corals, anemones, crinoids, basketstars or fishes specialized for capturing active prey can make use of detritus, although a number of coral species found in slightly deeper, quieter water have turned to detritus as the main source of food, thereby avoiding competition with plankton feeders. Lettuce coral is a good example of a detritus-feeding coral, with its broad, leaf-like expanses. Tiny interconnecting polyps transport detritus collected in mucus on the surface to the mouth, using tiny hairs, rather than tentacles.

Strange as it may seem, the worms we all know from our gardens have distant relatives in coral reefs that live in tubes and extend from these tubes a magnificent crown. One crown looks like a pair of tiny, brilliantly coloured Christmas trees, separated by a small colourful pad. Often these little trees adorn the top of a piece of coral, hiding the worm that lives beneath in a little calcium carbonate tube. The tube has been secreted by the worm and later the coral has grown over it. Divers often reach out to touch the delicate little trees only to find that they suddenly disappear into the tube, leaving a sharp spike sticking out. The worm has light-sensitive cells that sense the approach of danger and withdraws so rapidly that the human eye is unable to follow it.

Others of these so-called animal "flowers" include worms with crowns that look like feather dusters, and many of them are brilliantly coloured, varying from solid reds, yellows or oranges, to multi-hued varieties, some with delicate shades of pastel and contrasting tips on the branches. These most beautiful and delicate of the reef creatures are also garbage-disposal units, catching the drifting detritus in the fine divisions of the branches and by the gentle action of hairs on the crown carrying the material to the mouth.

Another tube-dwelling worm is designed to gather the debris from the bottom, but instead of having a small upright crown, the tentacles of this worm are like a little pile of exceptionally sticky and skinny, blue-grey noodles, stretched out along the bottom, oozing from one crevice to the next. From time to time one of the tentacles snakes back to the worm, where the accumulated detritus is removed and the tentacle sent drifting out again. The tentacles of a single worm can cover an area as large as thirty centimetres in diameter.

The rest of the reef debris is gathered by many small creatures. Some are crustaceans that resemble plankton, but which seem to spend their entire lives on the bottom. These are particularly numerous in the little eddies and crevices where the debris tends to collect, drifting there in the currents.

Considering the remarkable number of reef creatures that eat plankton, it is perhaps a little surprising that almost all reef animals produce young that pass at least some of their life in a planktonic stage, often drifting to new areas as larvae. The strategy most use to get by the numerous plankton feeders is simply to produce prodigious numbers of larvae. Larvae leave the reef when they are small, some spending most of their larval life in open water where the danger from

plankton feeders is considerably less than closer to a reef. Some may not leave the reef area at all. Because of the extreme difficulty of raising these creatures from eggs in artificial conditions, it is not even certain just how long the young are in a larval stage. If they do not leave, but are so small that they could not possibly resist the currents, how do they stay on the reef? Is their development so rapid that they do not have to be concerned about drifting away? Much research is needed to find out the answers to many questions about the behaviour of coral reef larvae.

From the cornucopia of open-ocean drifters such as tiny diatoms and dinoflagellates to the transparent larvaceans and hyperactive copepods, the reefs take a rich harvest and incorporate it into the most fundamental of the reef-building animals, corals, sponges and gorgonians. Hundreds of other species compete with the reef builders for a share of the resource. Even the water-borne detritus becomes part of the drifting riches gathered by the plankton feeders.

Chapter Five

Predator and Prey

For the reef, plankton from the open ocean is a free source of energy since the reef itself does not have to provide it with nutrients or space to receive light for photosynthesis. Phalanx after phalanx of plankton feeders scavenge the harvest from the open-ocean waters that sweep over the reef, capturing in the plankton not only energy, but also nutrients and minerals that the reef would otherwise have had to provide.

Because the reef is only a tiny proportion of the entire open ocean, the reduction in the open ocean material and energy supplies caused by the parasitism of the reef ecosystem is quite small. But for the reef it makes a critical difference. It has been calculated that coral reefs are one of the single most productive biological communities in the world. More animal and plant material is produced on a reef per unit of area per year than in almost any other place in the world, including cultivated cropland, partly because the offshore ocean is doing a great deal of the work the reef would otherwise have had to do.

Converting the riches of the ocean plankton into reef animals is achieved by a host of plankton pickers and sweepers, which then become food for predators. The first of the plankton pickers are schooling fishes, which then become prey for a small number of very prominent predators.

To catch a plankton picker like a fusilier fish, the predator must be very swift and accurate. Mackerels and jacks, both swift-swimming, leather-jacketed, and streamlined with narrow tails to slice through the water at great speed, hunt by cruising up and down the reef through schools of plankton pickers. In contrast to predators that lunge or dart out of hiding at their prey, these fish run their prey down. Their technique is to get between the school of plankton pickers and the reef, line up a potential member of the school as prey, then with muscles pulled like taut wires down the sides of their bodies, they flash in to the attack. Such a rush expends a great deal of energy, so these predators must carefully judge in advance whether or not the strike will succeed. All of the action is in high speed; the mackerels use their high-performance, narrow scissor tails to propel them at speeds no human swimmer could match. The mackerel cannot accelerate as quickly as some of the lurking predators, but these living thunderbolts can reach a speed in excess of forty kilometres per hour, and they can sustain it for a significant period of time. Speeds of this magnitude are very rare in underwater environments, because water is nearly eight hundred times as heavy as air.

None of the plankton pickers would win a race with a mackerel without a head start, so they must judge the predator's distance to know when the dive for cover must begin. The mackerel cruises into a school quickly, a technique that often makes it possible to approach to within the crucial distance before the school is aware. Water clarity is an important factor: in very clear water schools move much further from the reef than if the water is a little "murky," because it is easier for them to see a predator.

Jacks are not as fast as the mackerel, nor can they maintain high speeds for as long, so they use a method of attack halfway between the drift and lunge technique of the barracuda and that of the guided-missile mackerels. Mackerels swim high off the reef, whereas jacks often swim closer to the bottom, travelling in packs drifting slowly along the reef, until at some unseen signal they accelerate, swooping down to the reef, often making an audible thundering sound. Because the jacks were present all along, but not acting in a threatening manner, the schools of plankton pickers may not have been able to allow enough distance to reach the reef before the jacks intercept them. The schools close ranks and hold together until they reach cover, but any schooler that "panics" and breaks ranks is almost certainly finished.

When a pack of jacks or a mackerel is working a school of fusiliers, damselfish, or wrasses, the whole reef seems to be aware of it. A brittle tension can be felt, and a small army of groupers and snappers move restlessly out from under their coral caves, eyes turned carefully up to the sky, watching for silhouetted little fish to come shooting down for cover. Their best chance is a near-miss by the predators, because then the prey is acutely conscious of the danger rushing at it from behind and, while a fish can see almost a full sphere, its attention can focus too fully on the jack or mackerel to notice the grouper waiting in ambush.

While predation is a daily and common fact of life on a reef, the events are so swift that it is actually unusual to witness it. The basic impression a human visitor has is of all the creatures living happily and

Jacks, typified by the stiff, forked tail with armoured scutes, are among the most common high-speed predators. They cruise up and down the deep edge of reefs, preying on smaller plankton-picking fishes.

at ease with one another, of a harmonious and positive existence, with some inhabitants busier than others, some curious, some disinterested. In fact, the animals are finely tuned to avoid being in a position of compromise. A mistake in the fine tuning is usually fatal.

Both prey species and lurking predators have evolved camouflages to reduce the chances of being seen by each other. It is thought that, like humans, most animals have an "image" of what a fish looks like. Camouflage disguises the shape of the body and destroys the image of a "fish" by making it look like a part of the environment. One technique tatters the edges of the skin, as in the scorpionfish, so that the beginnings and ends of the fish are not apparent. A more common camouflage uses a pattern of bold blocks of colour which contrast sharply, but do not follow the shape of the body, thereby obliterating its image. Usually these blocks of colour run vertically or at oblique angles, and intersect parts of the fins, further reducing their recognizability.

Eyes are one of the most prominent features of animals, so disguises here are common. Matching the colour of the eye to the body is simple, but not always successful, because the eye has a different texture than the body. Many fish use a combination of obliterating blotches of colour and masking the eye with bold slashes of black or blue running across their faces and through the eye. Some eye masks are at odd angles, others run the length of the fish, beginning at the

snout, passing through the eye, across the gills, and onto the sides of the body.

Predators also disguise their eyes with lines of bold colour. Most of these lines are aimed at precisely the spot in front of the predator that a prey organism should be for maximum success of catching it; the line is like a rifle sight. When the line points directly at the prey, a mental trigger in the fish's brain fires, and, if all the other conditions are right, the fish lunges.

Often a predator's attention is drawn to an "eye" that is a very brilliant line of colour around a dark black blotch. The "eye" is not an eye at all, but merely a splotch of colour located on the tail, or on the dorsal fin, at the wrong end of the fish. The predator, like a duck hunter, anticipates that the prey will move slightly forward during the time it takes for the predator to cover the distance to the prey. If it aims at the false eye then it will have aimed at the wrong end, entirely missing the prey, which has meanwhile scooted off in a completely unexpected direction.

A few species, but not very many (or the trick would not work), have a special colour pattern on the fins, which they normally keep folded. When a predator rushes at one of them, it suddenly expands its fins, creating the mistaken impression that it is suddenly much bigger, a huge eye apparently staring at the predator from a large "head," which the predator had assumed (and correctly so) to be the whole

Many skin-divers report having seen sea snakes in the Atlantic, but in all instances where the report could be checked out, the "snake" has turned out to be a sand eel, which commonly wanders around on the reef. Its markings suggest a snake, but it is in fact a fish.

Colour patterns are often used to confuse predators. In this four-eyed butterflyfish, a false eye near the tail deceives the predator into striking at the wrong end of the fish.

fish. Even if the predator hesitates only momentarily, this is sufficient to allow the prey to escape.

Underwater creatures use warning patterns to suggest, indeed announce, that they are dangerous, like the lionfish and some of the deadly poisonous sea snakes which are found only in the Indo-Pacific. Warning colour patterns are most often bands of highly contrasting colour around the body. Yellow and black, white and black, or red and black are the most common, and seem to be universally recognized instinctively as warning colours. On the reef a few harmless creatures have adopted the deception of mimicking dangerous creatures, and therefore enjoying the same immunity as the dangerous animal. A small triggerfish has the same shape and colour pattern as a small reef puffer that has a deadly poison in the skin and internal organs. Predators taking reef puffers in their mouths immediately spit them out, presumably because of the bad taste, and soon learn to avoid them. The triggerfish, much less common than the puffer, relies on the chance that predators will have learned to avoid the colour pattern and shape of the poisonous fish before they chance to try the mimic.

It seems a paradox that many of the reef creatures are brightly coloured, indeed garish and bizarre, so bold that it is hard to imagine even a mad artist being able to mix and design a wilder colour pattern than those found on fishes abounding on coral reefs. Light under water is not the same as light in the air. Even in the clearest waters of the reef, it is exceptional to be able to see the length of a football field. Furthermore, the quality of the light changes drastically with the distance it travels through the water. Sunlight has the full range of colours from red through orange, yellow, green, blue, indigo and violet. As soon as sunlight (or even the light from a photographer's lamp) enters the water, both ends of the spectrum begin to be absorbed. In clear water, reds and violets can penetrate a distance of ten or fifteen metres. At a depth of twenty-five metres, the oranges have gone and even yellow is fading rapidly. By forty metres, only blue and a little green are left. This effect works both vertically and horizontally, much to the frustration of photographers.

People often suggest that perhaps the fish are more sensitive and can see colours we cannot. Perhaps, but it would not matter how sensitive their eyes were, the colour is simply not there for them to see. Why then are the fish and other creatures so brightly coloured when they are brought to the surface? Are the pigments not present at those depths? Yes, the pigments are present, but the light that will reflect from those pigments is not there, so they are not visible.

What then is the purpose of having the bright colours? It is a fact that species found in deeper waters tend to have more red and orange on them, just the colours that should not be visible. At least to human eyes, the fish at that depth take on hues of blue, green or brown. A startling but dramatic demonstration of the effect is often experienced by divers who inadvertently scratch themselves on coral and bleed a little from the cut. In water deeper than about ten metres, a person bleeds bright green blood, in which all trace of the red is gone.

Are the colours of fish accidental? Probably not. More likely the red pigments are used to block underlying pigments. If a blue fish is in a pure blue spectrum it would reflect all of the light that struck it. In our spectrum on the surface, only white reflects all the light. Underwater, the blue fish would stand out as brightly as a white flag on the land, a luminous beacon. By adding a wash of red pigment that absorbs light, the brightness of the colour is reduced. Why red, and not black? No one knows.

Light in the water also diffuses much more quickly than in air, because particles in the water reflect light back towards the source or off to the side. After a remarkably short distance it is extremely difficult to see a thin line in the water. Many fish have intricate and fine patterns of lines on them. Viewed up close underwater, the lines are distinct and clear, used perhaps to ensure that the opposite sex can recognize a potential mate without question. Viewed at a distance, the lines blur into one another, the pattern becomes a diffuse colour blending into the background. Ingeniously, the same colour pattern serves two different purposes depending entirely on where the viewer is located.

Colour patterns appear to serve little purpose on the tube worms that feed on detritus; they certainly are not used to attract mates, since the worms never leave their tubes, and predators, if human eyes can judge, should easily be able to pick them out. Some butterflyfish, with long snouts equipped with pincer jaws, feed on the crowns of these worms. These little fish are extremely flattened from side to side and have stiff spines in the dorsal fin, making them an uncomfortable mouthful for a predator. They often have both false eye spots and obliterative colour patterns on the body.

In the same fish family as the butterflyfish, the angelfish are almost unique in that they feed on sponges. Despite the fact that these plankton-feeders have been around for about four-to five hundred million years, very few animals have been able to stomach them successfully. In fact, angelfish are a highly evolved group of fishes, suggesting that the invention of a system to digest sponges and not be bothered by their glass spicules and noxious chemicals is very recent. These brightly coloured and graceful fish are also a bit fussy over which species they will eat, preferring the soft sponges to those that have leathery outer layers.

Oddly, there are almost no fish that prey on the seemingly very vulnerable and poorly armed gorgonians. Occasionally a butterflyfish will nip at the gorgonians and soft corals, but on the whole gorgonians are not subject to great depredations by fishes, or indeed by many other animals. There seems no obvious reason why they are not eaten by a wide variety of animals, because they do not have powerful nematocysts. Both sponges and encrusting fire coral often overgrow the branches of gorgonians, outcompeting them for the stem they have built.

One animal that does eat gorgonians is the snail. The sea fan is a gorgonian made up of many very small polyps which feed largely on tiny plant cells or on detritus. All of these tiny polyps are intermeshed into a lattice-work colony that can grow as tall as two metres. A beautiful snail called the flamingo tongue hides during the day and comes out at night, spreading a delicate orange mantle over its back. It crawls slowly up the sea fan, scraping and digesting polyps on its way, leaving a brown trail of destruction. It is an interesting philosophical question whether the snail is a predator or a parasite. It kills polyps, but does not kill the colony. Parasites kill parts of the host by eating or digesting them, but they do not usually kill the host (if they are well-adjusted parasites).

While gorgonians and sponges, which might seem to be simple prey to tackle, enjoy a certain measure of immunity from predators, corals are prized prey for many species. Parrotfish scrape the corals, removing polyp and skeleton, often leaving a double groove on the surface. Opinion is divided on whether they eat the coral to get the zoox anthellae or to use the polyp, but whatever the case, they represent one of the most abundant of all fish on a reef, and are responsible for a great amount of coral erosion and its conversion into sand. Experiments done on one reef in Barbados in the West Indies found that erosion due to parrotfish amounted to nearly half a million grams per year on a small reef about one hundred metres square. Some damselfish and a few wrasses from the Pacific regularly feed on coral polyps as well. Many species of butterflyfish specialize in scraping the polyps out of their little cups, leaving the coral skeleton intact. This is particularly true of several types of butterflyfish which seem to form permanent pairs and are territorial, defending one or two large heads of coral as their own. The coral is able to regenerate when the skeleton is not destroyed, and new polyps take over. This means that the butterflyfish is treating the coral as a renewable resource, ensuring that its food supply will not be destroyed.

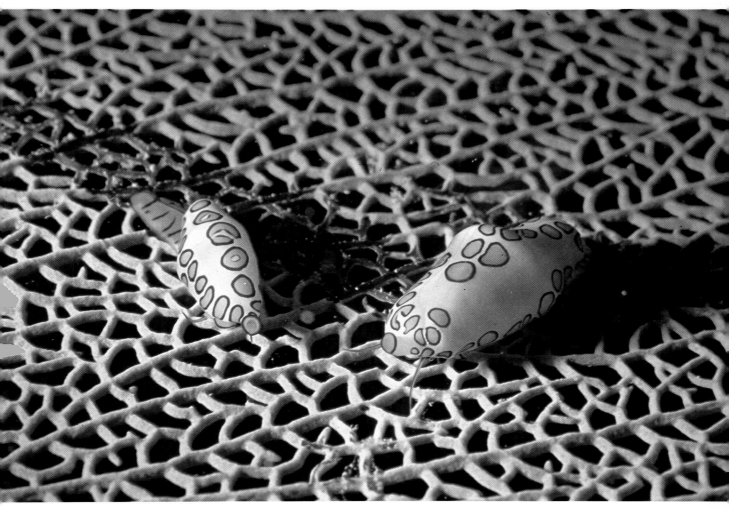

Other fish are not so careful. Triggerfish and filefish use their very powerful jaws and heavy teeth to snap the tips off branching corals. Even one or two species of puffers, which also have prodigious teeth and powerful jaw muscles, are adapted to feed on the tips of branching coral species. Pieces of coral up to two centimetres in length have been found in the stomach of one species of puffer on the Australian Great Barrier Reef. There is even one report of a blenny, usually a strict herbivore, eating coral polyps.

Fishes are not the only creatures that eat corals. Nudibranchs and several species of starfish are capable of scraping or digesting the polyps out of their little cups. The crown-of-thorns starfish which is normally rare and restricted to deep water has recently increased greatly in numbers and moved into shallower waters. This starfish can reach up to thirty or forty centimetres in diameter, and is covered with large, sharp and poisonous spines. In a single night, an adult can eat the polyps of a complete coral head ten to twenty centimetres across, destroying months or even years of growth.

One of the few predators on gorgonians is the orange flamingo tongue, a snail which hides in the daytime, but comes out at night to feed, particularly on sea fans.

To disguise their shape and better blend into the background, many fish, such as this spotted drum, use bars or spots of highly contrasting colours to disrupt their outline.

The starfish problem was first noticed in 1970 at Guam, where they had digested nearly ninety per cent of the corals on one side of the island. Filamentous algae grew in riots where corals had been, fish and other creatures that depended on the corals disappeared, and the ecosystem fell apart. Attempts to organize the local residents to kill the starfish were fraught with great troubles. The poisonous spines made handling them dangerous, and because of the peculiar ability of starfish to regenerate completely from fragments, it only made things worse to try to cut them up under water. Eventually, the starfish declined because they had eaten most of the coral polyps, which are their food. Controversy remains whether this is one of a series of natural cycles of changes in the abundance of the crown-of-thorn starfish, or whether it is induced by man's interference. Areas where the starfish were not very abundant seem to have recovered within a period of a few years, but it is still far too early to predict how long it will take for the devastated reefs to recover, or if they will ever be the same. Serious planners are worried that tropical atolls may be in jeopardy because the protective growing part of the coral has been destroyed, allowing the waves and normal biological eroders, such as fish, sea urchins and creatures that drill into the coral, to gain the upper hand in the balance between the growth and destruction that is so much a part of the dynamic system of a reef.

Until very recently it was thought (and even now some hold to the traditional view) that the more complex an ecosystem gets, the more stable it becomes. The argument is simple: in a food web where there are very few links, a break in any one of them is a very large proportion of the system; whereas in a complex system, where there are many links, the loss of one is not as important. This logic is correct for some animal and plant communities. Truly diverse communities, however, depend on a plant or animal creating a new physical

92   THE CORAL REEF

Experienced divers carefully avoid the long, sharp and brittle spines of the black sea urchin, Diadema, *which occasionally has a partly white colour variant. A small arrow crab hides among the spines of these two sea urchins.*

environment. In an atoll, the original flat surface of the submerged mountain is no longer the habitat which provides living space and places to hide, reproduce and hunt. Instead, corals, gorgonians and sponges with their vertical trunks, horizontal branches, and intricate caves provide these opportunities. Furthermore, the corals, sponges and gorgonians are living things that respond and adjust to the demands placed on them by the creatures that live in and perhaps even feed on them. What was the flat, smooth side of a mountain has been changed to an intricate three-dimensional environment in which the very "soil" is alive and responsive. The places where animals live, hunt, reproduce and die exist because a living organism built them.

This dynamic interaction with a responsive environment (including gorgonians, sponges and corals) which creates and maintains space makes possible the very large number of species found in reefs (or in any other community in which the environment is largely a result of a living organism — such as forests). So the community is most vulnerable if anything attacks this organic base; it is an attack on the very fibre of the system. In a coral reef there are many cross-connections between food webs, and unexpected reactions to the alteration of a seemingly unimportant link can often cause a dramatic change in the community. The vastly destructive effects of the crown-of-thorns starfish is an illustration of one small altered link. Even such extremely rich and diverse systems as coral reefs are inherently unstable because they are in a constant state of adjustment, living on continually new balances, responding to new pressures. The responses are not easy to predict. Anything that destroys the critical reef-builders, such as corals, can potentially unbalance the whole reef system.

Some very unusual organisms invade coral skeletons. Undoubtedly the most effective driller is the sea urchin. Hiding

Sea urchins in Barbados were calculated to produce a little less than two grams of sand per day each. Twenty-three sea urchins per square metre produced a little less than fifty grams per square metre per day. In a year, these spiny black urchins degraded to sand about 17.5 kilograms of coral in one square metre.

inconspicuously out of the way in the day, this creature can actually chew its way right into a very large boulder of coral. Once inside, the sea urchin continues to chomp and grind away eating the coral until it is reduced to a hollow ball. As the top and sides crumble, the reef top becomes a jagged and craggy mass of small spires and ragged hills. This surface is rapidly covered with coralline and filamentous algae, which in turn are fed on or reduced to sand by the urchins.

Many other organisms drill and excavate into the coral skeleton. Worms have grinding jaws to core out small tubes or cavities as a home. One worm, a sipunculid, is a master of the boring habit. As well as worms, specialized clams also drill large holes through the coral, so riddling it with holes that a good smack will shatter it. Unlike most clams that feed by drawing plankton or detritus into their mantle cavity, these clams take the rock borings into their mouths and release it into the body cavity, eventually pumping out digested pellets of rock.

Perhaps the most unexpected driller is the sponge. It drills into coral limestone using chemical secretions and by pushing on the weakened walls of the resulting crevices. An amazing number of sponges do this, but are noticeable only as smears of colour on coral boulders. Filamentous algae also are capable of drilling down into the corals, by processes that are not yet completely understood. If a piece of algae-infested coral is split, sometimes two layers of algae are found, one a few millimetres into the limestone, the other one several centimetres deep. It is a wonder the plant cells get enough light here to make photosynthesis possible.

Fungi, surprisingly, can cause considerable erosion from the limestone skeleton of a reef. These reef fungi are the same forms found invading forest plants and moist corners of old houses, and seem to be able to handle salt water as easily as air. Fungi make their way through the coral by first secreting a chemical that dissolves the limestone. Minute fungal hairs (hyphae) slowly make their way through the coral until it is riddled with small tunnels and valleys, some of them interconnecting. Hyphae throttle small pieces of coral in incredible slow motion, pinching them off to form fragments of sand.

Worms, clams, sponges, algae and fungi are capable of destroying nearly twenty kilograms of coral per square metre per year. Adding up all of the major rock-destroying (sand-producing) organisms including fishes and sea urchins, the total is a remarkable fifty kilograms of limestone eroded into sand per square metre per year in the shallow-water parts of the reef. To hold its own, the reef must constantly respond, and produce enough new growth to replace the destroyed corals. It is indeed a delicate balance.

Chapter Six
Signals Between Species

The first systematic record of the world's different plants and animals was attempted by Aristotle, after whose work, science nearly disappeared for almost 1,500 years. Inquiry flowered again in the mid 1700s, when a botanist named Linnaeus devised a scheme to classify all living things by scientific name—a system that is still in use today.

How could such a wonderful interplay of forces between so many vastly different kinds of plants and animals come to be? Where did all the creatures come from, and why are there so many? Ever since we first questioned our own origins, we have asked how the world we know has developed into what it is today. No scientist would pretend to have all the answers to these essentially philosophical questions, but it is possible to offer answers to parts of those questions.

In 1859, Charles Darwin described a theory in which it was possible to explain how so many plants and animals came to be different one from another. His ideas were in sharp contrast to the teachings of his society at the time, and because they appeared to call religious truths into question, his theory did not then and does not now enjoy full popular support. For most scientists, however, it offered answers to questions, and, more important, it allowed them to continue to question.

The concept of evolution is a simple one. It begins with the observation that animals of a given type (species) look alike, with discernible differences between members. A second observation is that some animals can live in conditions that are unfavourable for others, even within the same species; a result of the observed differences. These differences are often passed from parents to offspring, but sometimes new, minor differences crop up in the offspring. If a part of the population happens to get separated from the rest, it carries with it a range of minor inheritable variations as well as the ability to introduce new minor variations. The individuals that survive best in the new environment will be those that happen to have minor variations that best fit the surrounding conditions. Perhaps some of their offspring will have variations that make them even more comfortable and successful. If so, they will be the most likely to survive and have young. Over a long period of time, this naturally occurring selection could make them look quite different to the original population. If they are sufficiently different by the time they rejoin the original population, they will not be able to interbreed. From one species there will have become two.

It may be difficult to believe that the whole of the plant and animal world, with its millions of species, could have developed through such a simple mechanical process. The secret is time. Over millions of years, the gradual response to pressures of survival requirements, the marvellous ability of living things to make adjustments, has created a wonderful array of animals and plants.

How long does it take for a new species to form? In the Great Lakes of North America, there are unique species found nowhere else, and which must have evolved in the lakes. But the Great Lakes were buried under a sheet of ice three kilometres thick until the end of the last ice age, so they could not have been in existence for more than 15,000 years. If the species in the Great Lakes could evolve in less than 15,000 years, there are undoubtedly animals or plants that could have evolved in less time in more favourable conditions. In other cases it may take much longer.

A number of Caribbean species look similar to eastern Pacific species. They probably came from the same original population when the Central American subcontinent was still lying under the warm salty waters of a continuous ocean between what are now the Caribbean and the Pacific, some 2.5 million years ago. Some species never seem to change no matter how many separate populations there are. One strange little creature called a brachiopod (*Lingula*), lives in the mud and looks a bit like a clam. It is virtually identical to its ancient forebears of the dim distant past, 100 million years ago.

In Hawaii, the Australian Great Barrier Reef, in the south Pacific islands, islands in the Indian Ocean and even in the Red Sea, there are a number of species that are found nowhere else and must have evolved there. Geologists have provided an explanation of how the separations of population were possible. The ocean floor is composed of a mass of gigantic plates of the earth's crust. Each plate rides on the earth's plastic mantle, and as they move around, they carry continents with them, pressing up mountains in front and leaving a widening split behind, a split marked by the underwater volcanic mountains that provide new areas for coral reefs to develop. India, for example, was once near where Australia is located today. As it travelled to its present location, the islands of Chagos, Maldives, Laccadives, Seychelles and Mauritius were left in its wake. Over millions of years and thousands of such events in the world's oceans, it is thought that the entire spectrum of reef creatures developed.

The number of different species on a reef is staggering. In many of the reefs in the New Guinea-Australia area (where the numbers of species reach a maximum) there may be as many as 2,000 species of fish, and the total of all the different kinds of animals and plants including micro and single-celled organisms, may easily run to over 50,000. It is presumed that the maximum number of separations of populations over the longest period of time has taken place in this region. Away from this central area the number of different species on each reef declines. If there are about 2,000 species of fish on a New Guinea reef, in a reef of comparable size in the middle of the Indian Ocean, or far out in the south Pacific, the number of species may be reduced to 1,000 or less. There are exceptions to this rule; a secondary flowering of species has taken place in Hawaii, the Red Sea, the Caribbean, and the islands of Micronesia.

The Caribbean has a moderately rich reef species count, even though it is a long way from the New Guinea area. Even here, however, there are very few new "groups" of animals or plants even in the Caribbean that cannot trace their roots to the New Guinea area, suggesting an origin that goes back to the break up of Pangaea. The intriguing soft corals which are so abundant in the Pacific and Indian Oceans are exceptionally rare in the Caribbean, usually found in deep water only. The giant clams, successful in the entire Indo-Pacific, never made it to the Caribbean. Within the fishes, whole families are missing—anemonefish, flatheads, emperors and vast schools of fusilier fish. It is not that the correct environment is missing in the Caribbean; experiments in aquaria (no one really wants to try it in nature for fear of disastrous results) have shown that anemonefish can live happily in the Caribbean anemones, and the cleaner wrasses from the Pacific seem to be able to teach Atlantic species that they are acceptable barbers.

A proposal to build a sea-level canal between the Caribbean and the eastern Pacific across Panama worries biologists, because they are not sure what would happen if the two communities were mixed. Would the poisonous sea snakes from the Pacific enter the Caribbean and succeed there? Experiments conducted on corals have shown first colonizers in the Pacific to be extremely aggressive, whereas the species on the Caribbean side were not as aggressive, suggesting that Pacific species might take over with unknown results. Species that were once members of the same populations, but are now separated from each other are presently considered to be unable to reproduce together, but could they compete in ways that would be detrimental to the reefs? Another worry is that twin species from each side of Panama may be able to reproduce together after all, and nobody really knows what the consequence might be from such unions. The young may die before they hatch or like the mule (the offspring of a horse/donkey mating) may be sterile, or the adults may not provide the correct signals to allow courtship and spawning.

Reproductive barriers isolating one population from another are the subject of a great deal of research because this is what decides whether the populations have become different species. But the decision rests with the animals, not with scientists. We can only guess

whether the differences are large enough to prevent reproduction taking place if the populations are put together under natural conditions.

Animals have no difficulty telling each other apart, whereas it may be very difficult for a human to distinguish them. Often a scientist will spend hours measuring little fin rays, or counting the number of spines on a claw, or recording minute differences in colour patterns. Then, taking the mass of data collected, he submits it to a gigantic computer that will show whether on the basis of a statistical analysis, the two populations can be distinguished. The animals concerned, however, have no trouble making the decision quickly, so they must use a cue not necessarily easily visible to the human eye. They are somehow communicating a message to one another that they are one particular species, and no other.

Brightly coloured tropical bristle worms advertise their needle-sharp, glass-like spines, which cause a burning sensation when touched. Sharp pincer jaws can shoot out to catch small prey.

Communication is common in animals, between simple creatures such as worms, snails and starfish, as well as in the elaborate messages communicated between members of the crustaceans, such as crabs and lobsters, and among the fishes. One of the simplest and yet most important questions that animals ask each other is: "Are you the same species as I am?" A signal in answer must be both received and understood.

For creatures like worms, the signal may be as simple as being in the same place at precisely the same time. The palolo worm which lives in the reefs of the Pacific and West Indies inhabits tubes in the coral, and as the correct time approaches, arranges itself to face backwards out of the burrow. In the Pacific, one day before the first day of the last quarter of the October-November moon, the eggs and sperm in this worm begin to ripen rapidly. The next night as the waning moon rises over the water, the palolo mysteriously senses the time and breaks off the back half of its body, which then swims frantically to the surface. On these nights, the water writhes with huge numbers of the fragments. Suddenly on an unseen, unknown signal, the fragments of the worm explode and the water turns milky with masses of eggs and sperm. In the West Indies, this spectacular event takes place on the night of the beginning of the third quarter of the June-July moon. Back in the burrow, the worms regenerate the lost half easily, but the ripening of eggs or sperm does not occur again until the following year at precisely the same time.

In a few worms, males and females meet and recognize each other not by touch or sight, but by smell. A powerful aromatic chemical secreted by the female can be recognized by and is attractive only to the male of the same species.

In animals that see well, such as crabs and fishes, shape and colour may be key factors in recognition of the species. Crustacean eyes are very different to the eyes of a fish (or a human), being composed of tiny facets, each of which forms a part of the image. These mosaic images are extremely sensitive to motion, but shape and colour are poorly perceived when not in motion. To draw attention to the colour pattern on the claws, or perhaps to their shape, male crabs face the females head on, and wave the claws in front of their faces. By watching the claws shake up and down, the female is able to judge whether the male is the correct species. Recognizing the species is automatic: the animals do not mentally weigh the evidence as a scientist might, they simply respond to the correct signal and do not respond to the wrong signal.

Several tiny gobies disguise their body shapes using vertical bands or bars. To make the body disguise work, only a single pattern would have been necessary, but instead each species has a unique design. Species may have solid bars against a pale background, pale bars against a dark background, a few heavy, bold bars, bars dark in the middle with pale edges, or the other way around. In the most elaborate designs, the bars are composites of alternating dark and light. For each goby, an inherited key signal is used to recognize its own species; it does not have to recognize the others, it has only to reject anything that does not have the right pattern.

Not all fish display their distinctive patterns at all times. Three strategies are used to hide pigment patterns used for species recognition which would interfere with their daily life style. The first is to have a distinctive colour pattern hidden on a fin, which is erected only when an answer to the question of identity is demanded. These patterns are usually bold and startling, so they must remain hidden from predators until they are needed. Damselfish hide their colour pattern using skin cells that contain coloured pigments, and which can expand or contract in a matter of seconds. Adults may be relatively bland in normal appearance, but on the approach of a prospective spawning partner, the male damselfish expands the special cells quickly, and, blushing with new and exotic colours, advances boldly towards the female. If danger threatens, or if he is rejected, the pattern disappears almost as quickly as it was assumed. A different pattern may show if instead of a prospective mate, the approaching fish turns out to be another male. In both cases, the fish change colour quickly to proclaim their identity, and to state what their immediate future action will be, either courtship or aggression.

Colours are not the only signal a fish can produce to communicate messages. The positions of the fins, whether raised or lowered, are important signals, even if they have no special markings. The fish can raise its fins to look as big and fierce as possible, and many reef fishes use this as a signal of aggression. Its opposite, all the fins lowered and held close to the body, is a signal of submission. In a fight, fish raise their fins, sometimes elaborating this raised fin display with a change in body position. Elongate fishes tend to face each other, holding their bodies parallel to the other fish in the shape of an S. In fishes which are not elongate, an aggressive posture is one with the head held pointing towards the bottom, tail up in the water. Most often, a mere threat is sufficient to defeat the intruder, who, to avoid getting hurt, communicates that he has given up by lowering his fins, turning slowly around and carefully retreating from the area. The owner is supposed to respect the surrender and allow the fish to retreat unharmed, although often the owner will give the tail a little nip, to emphasize the victory.

A series of graduated signals can communicate degrees of aggression. In the bicolor damselfish from the Caribbean, one of the best-studied species, there are three types of signals used: colour, position of the fins and body, and sound. The colour pattern is dark on the front half of the body and head, separated obliquely from a pale back half and tail. When the fish is aggressive, the amount of dark colour increases and a vertical pale bar appears on the side through the dark colour. The action and position of the fins and body are also expressive, beginning with a mere turning to look at the intruder. As aggression rises, the fish turns to face the intruder head on, then advances, with fins rising to a fully erect position. Once the fish gets close enough, it turns to the side so that the full extent of the spread fins and staring eye can be appreciated by the intruder. If this is not sufficient, the little fish advances closer and turning sideways again,

Although most squirrelfish remain hidden in the daytime, the longjaw squirrelfish often hovers outside a cave. If closely approached by a diver it emits a clearly audible drumming sound which is intended as a threat.

beats on the side of the intruding fish with his tail. If even this fails the bicolor resorts to its last defense and bites the intruder's fins, eyes and scales. It is rare indeed that this is not sufficient to drive out the other fish, or, in some cases, an intruding diver. In another species of damselfish, the beau gregory, the defending fish bites the ground, scooping up a mouthful of sand which it spits out in front of the intruder. This redirected biting is an advance warning of where the bite will be aimed next.

Not all of the damselfish's threats are directed towards a single intruder, nor does the intruder have to be of the same species, although the largest territories are defended against members of its own species. Its threats also seem to be directed against species that would make use of the same resources in its territory. The bicolor, when confronted with a school or group of intruders, cannot bite them all or give them all a personal threat, so it displays by standing on its head. The blue chromis, another Caribbean species, performs this display directly over the nest of eggs. This somehow ridiculous definition of the exact position of the eggs seems silly, but fish of other species seem to recognize the position as a threat. Whether this knowledge has been acquired by being bitten, or is inherited is unknown.

In addition to the movements and colour changes, the bicolor is capable of producing sounds from within its body. The first sound does little more than announce its presence and the species to which it belongs. In recordings, the sound is like a chirp or click. On rising levels of aggression, the fish can produce a single low-pitched thump, or even a succession of thumps that sound like a drumming sound to the human ear. Drumming is also used in courtship, and the time interval between each of the thumps is different for each different species of damselfish. One unusual noise the fish makes, whose exact meaning is unclear, sounds like a baby's rattle, followed by a pop.

Damselfish are not unusual in having the ability to make sounds, and many reef species have much more elaborate mechanisms for doing so. High-pitched sounds produced underwater tend to travel much further than low-pitched sounds. These low-pitched sounds are important in communicating threats or in courting, because while they can be powerful sounds up close, they do not carry far enough to attract the attention of predators, which might take advantage of the courting pair while their attention was diverted. It is almost a secret sound.

In the little cardinalfish, a set of muscles is attached to the swim bladder. The little fish pulls and relaxes the muscles quickly so that the swim bladder, normally just a bag of gas housed in the body of the fish to serve as a flotation organ, is made to expand and contract quickly. These are like the pulses a drummer pounds into the skin of his drum, except that instead of hitting the drum, it is being plucked. These sounds are transmitted through the water very effectively, and can be heard by the human ear.

The triggerfish, however, has a true drum. An extension of the swim bladder reaches through the rib cage and presses up against the outer skin just in front of the pectoral (side) fin. This skin is especially flexible, but also has lumpy scales on it. To play this drum, the fish raises its pectoral fin and brings it down quite smartly and repeatedly on the flexible piece of skin, beating on its chest. The swim bladder also has muscles attached to it and is remarkably thickened. Scientists have yet to make a careful study of the messages triggerfish send out with this elaborate mechanism.

At night the ocean over the reef is full of weird sounds, including one that sounds for all the world like a duck quacking. These are made by squirrelfish and are among the few fish sounds that change pitch (from low to high in this case) while they are being produced. Many can make the sounds loudly or softly. While most are used for aggressive encounters, some sounds warn of approaching danger. Whether these sounds are produced intentionally is not known, but schooling fishes commonly produce a thump when they rush away from a predator. The same sounds recorded and played back to the fish when there is no danger make them flee in a panic.

Producing a warning of any kind is or can be a dangerous business, especially if it takes any time or energy away from escaping. But one warning technique has been found in which once a fish is injured or killed, the juices that spread from the wounds, or leak from the predator's mouth, contain a special chemical which can be sensed by other fish, sometimes only by the same species. First found by a German scientist who named the substance "schreckstoff," the chemical causes other fish to be frightened and to flee. Not every species produces it and its exact nature is not yet known.

Communicating at night is very difficult, and most animals do not bother. A few remarkable creatures signal each other using lights. The light source is similar to that used by lightning bugs and glow-worms. It is usually produced by single-celled creatures that live in specially constructed containers called photophores within the animal's body. One small group of reef worms uses light-producing organs to recognize each other. Each species has its own code, just as in terrestrial insects. One of the mud-dwelling brittle starfish uses light signals, but it is not known for what purpose. They lie buried in the fine sediment at the base of reefs, two or three of their arms pointing up into the water, with pinpoints of light moving up and down the arms in a graceful pattern. Whether this is intended to attract plankton for feeding, or whether it is a species recognition signal is not known.

The best equipped of the reef nighttime light signallers is the flashlight fish, found in very shallow waters of the Red Sea. A species related to it was recently found at the base of reefs in the Caribbean, but only in depths greater than forty or fifty metres, too deep for safe diving at night. The shallow-water Red Sea form however, can be observed without even entering the water. One scientist spent a portion of her studies watching the schools by driving along the shoreline and counting the number of schools she could see flashing on and off, to try and estimate the abundance of the fish. The light organ is very large and powerful, located under the eye, with a hood that allows it to be flicked on and off. In addition to turning off and on, the light appears to be focussed so that the fish may actually use the light as a flashlight, pointing it around automatically in the direction it is heading, just like the headlights of an automobile. The fish, about ten centimetres long, is jet black. A school of them, showing only a multitude of brilliant spots of light winking on and off must be very confusing for the would-be nighttime predator.

True knowledge of what happens at night on a reef is only very recent. Previously, scientists deduced which were the night-active creatures from fishing or dredging, or from observing the cave-dwelling fishes during the day. The first real studies done by scientists working underwater on a reef using diving gear were published in 1968, and it has since been established that a nearly complete changeover of active species takes place in the night. Dusk and dawn in the tropics last only minutes, and the transition between the day shift and the night shift of animals on a reef is often accomplished in less than half an hour. The fish that were obvious on the reef in the day, rushing around, picking plankton, scraping algae or coral polyps and ranging in schools, are no longer to be seen. Most small plankton-picking damselfish and wrasses rest in crevices, under sponges and in caves at night. Unlike the cave dwellers seen in the daytime, these fish at night are propped up against the coral, or lying canted off to one side. Except that their eyes are not shut, they act as

if asleep. Fish that would not allow a diver closer than three or four metres in the day can actually be picked up at night. Even big parrotfish and giant turtles sleep back in the caves. Massive schools of grunts are gone, and spread out over the lagoon; familiar cave fishes like wrasses, sweepers and squirrelfish are no longer seen.

In place of all the daytime creatures, there are unfamiliar forms prowling the reef, which itself has a different appearance. The tentacles of the corals open up and spread waiting to catch plankton, imparting a fuzzy, indistinct look to the bottom. Brain corals are hardly recognizable from star corals. Crawling around on the bottom and up onto the gorgonians are creatures the daytime visitor never sees. Shrimps, their eyes brilliantly reflecting the torchlights, slipper lobsters, crabs and snails both big and small move carefully by. Familiar daytime predators, like groupers, are well back in the caves. Barracuda hang suspended and blind in the water, like spear-snouted javelins tensely aware of the light, ready to burst into panicked flight in some unpredictable direction—a real danger to the diver. Moray eels desert their caves and slither along the sand between the corals. Prowling, they can be seen to sense small damselfish resting quietly, and flashing forward, snatch them with recurving teeth that will not let go. Unfamiliar forms are there, too. The weirdly flattened soapfish, despite its small eyes, makes its way competently through the underwater tangle and in complete confidence dives on the slumbering damselfish, sucking them down easily.

Although daytime plankton pickers or algae grazers can be recognized, they look different; the colour patterns at night are blotchy and heavily barred, indicating that the star and moonshine on a reef is strong enough that night-resting fish need to use obliterative patterning. On several species with false eyes, the false eye disappears at night, suggesting that deceptive patterns do not work then, perhaps because the sleeper would not see the predator attracted to the false eye. Some parrotfish have a unique method of avoiding detection at

Hidden in caves, or sometimes in the holds of wrecked ships, fish such as these sweepers rest in large schools in the daytime. At night they leave their schools, swimming over the darkened reef to feed on plankton.

night; every night they build a cocoon of mucus that obliterates the recognizable parrotfish characters from marauding morays. Cocoons are discarded in the morning, when they are covered with debris.

One of the most effective devices for hiding is that used by some of the busy wrasses, which bury themselves completely in the sand, where they are almost immune from predators. Evidence that huge predators come to the reef at night can be seen the next morning on sand patches, where large pits appear overnight, the work of very big sting rays digging in the sand for a peculiar type of sea urchin that spends most of its time under the sand. These rays may reach 1.5 to 2 metres across the wings and dig pits equally wide. Their teeth take the form of a brick pavement rolled into a slight curve, and are used to crush the urchins or clams dug out of the sand.

In addition to the large predators active in the night reef, there are many small predators. Cardinalfish drift in the water, scooting and darting after small night-active crustaceans or even small fishes like night-feeding herring or silversides. The occasional snapper, its large eyes enabling it to see well enough to be a predator, lumbers by, and a few big squirrelfish remain on the reef instead of travelling to the passes and lagoon.

From the deep waters, large sharks, including such apparently lazy types as nurse sharks with their whisker-like, bottom-sensing barbels at the edge of their mouths, drift in to scavenge and pounce on unsuspecting sleeping fishes. Powerful beasts sometimes more than twice the length and five or ten times the weight of a man, such as the tiger and bull sharks, with cruel and slicing teeth drive in quickly and range rapidly up and down the reef, taking on even the largest prey. Early in the evening, hammerheads sometimes swim quickly by. Hammerhead sharks have eyes placed far out on the ends of hammer-shaped heads to allow them a combination of an extremely accurate aim, because of the widely spaced eyes, and rapid manoeuvrability, the result of the flattened and expanded head acting like a hydrofoil in the water. These characteristics make them exceptionally effective predators on smaller fishes.

Turtles often come onto the reef at night and push themselves into caves hoping that a tiger will not find them. While a tiger shark would not hesitate to attack a turtle, they are not capable of thoroughly investigating caves, because unlike many other kinds of fish, they are not built to swim in reverse. If they stick their heads into a cave, they can only get out by turning around. Furthermore, they cannot breathe through their gills if they stop swimming for long periods of time.

Sharks captured at night have been found to have a variety of fish in their stomachs, such as parrotfish, groupers and snappers, as well as squid. It is exceptionally difficult to study the habits of these dangerous creatures at night on the reef while diving, although a few people have done it, so the predatory methods that sharks use at night are not well known. With a few notable exceptions, few scientists have ever encountered sharks at night, despite the fact it is known they are more common on the reef at night than in the daytime. This suggests that sharks avoid the lights at night.

With the approach of dawn, the large sharks and rays begin to drift away from the reef. Grunts and snappers gather from their feeding grounds over the sand and grass flats to form small gatherings near the periphery of the reef. With the first light, all of these fish stream back to their daytime caves or schooling areas along a few paths. Waiting surreptitiously on the rush-hour routes, groupers, barracuda, lizard- and trumpetfish lie in ambush for unwary returning prey to become their day's breakfast. Wrasses cautiously rise out of the sand and dart into the reef for protection. In less than half an hour, the day shift is back on the reef.

Many fishes, such as these surgeon fish, feed actively in the daytime, and rest in coral crevices at night, often changing the normally uniform daytime colour to a blotchy pattern which blends in better with the moonlit background.

Chapter Seven

A Delicate Balance

Except for muddy delta and river-mouth areas, most shallow water warmer than 20°C is reef, including entire islands and their near-shore bottom. Because of the many food webs and the fact that the reef community takes a major portion of its energy and materials "free of charge" from the open ocean, coral reefs annually produce a weight of animals and plants that rivals or even surpasses the best croplands. In some islands, the entire economy and life of the people depend directly on the reef. This aquatic harvest supports many tropical countries and even considered on a world scale, much of the sea's bounty is derived from coral reefs. Plants are harvested for both food and industrial purposes.

Molluscs, including large snails, octopus and clams are a major commerce in some islands. Lobsters, crabs and shrimps, sea urchins, and even worms are important—tasty items for local and distant tables. Native peoples skin dive, or wade in shallow water at night looking for octopus, hooking them out of caves with a gig. The shells of snails or clams are also used to make ornaments or tools, and pretty shells may be collected carefully and sold as curios, either locally or by exporting to Europe and North America.

Undoubtedly the most valuable harvest from the sea is fish. Literally hundreds of species are harvested from coral reefs, and they can be the major source of protein for island and sea-side communities, as well as a very valuable exportable resource. Most native fishing is done using hand lines, with a baited hook and the line wound around a

In the Philippines, where there is a program of aquaculture, bits of certain types of edible seaweed are twisted into the twine of a very long rope, which is then returned to the sea. The ropes are drawn up periodically and the seaweed, which has grown quickly, is then harvested.

plastic bottle or piece of wood. Aside from cost, one reason for this is that a struggling fish in the water attracts other predators. If the fish is not dragged out as quickly as possible, sharks are certain to get at least half the prize. Another effective method uses traps constructed of wire mesh. A funnel-shaped entrance makes it simple for the fish to find their way in but hard to find the way back. Unfortunately, if the fisherman loses the trap, it continues to fish and the trapped fish then slowly starve to death. Lost traps are constantly rebaited with the dying fish and kill continuously for years. They are outlawed in a few areas, but widespread in most of the Caribbean. If trap losses are large, as in a storm, the population of fish can be seriously reduced over a period of years.

Native fishermen often display extraordinary skill in the use of cast nets — circular nets with the outer circumference weighted by lead shot. Heavy strings draw the outer edges together after the net has been thrown in the water. Draping the net over one arm, the fisherman walks slowly along the beach looking for a school of small fish. Using a smooth and graceful motion, the fisherman sends the net skimming airborne over the water spreading into a full circle, until just over the school it settles to the water, trapping the fish. It looks very simple, but a beginner presents a ludicrous sight, seemingly intent on catching himself rather than anything in the sea.

Very large beach seines hang like a wall of fine mesh netting in the water. They are spread in a loop from one spot on the shore to another. One line from the top of the net and one line from the bottom are used to draw the wall of netting towards the beach. The net may be over a hundred metres long, so a whole village sometimes draws the net to the shore, after which a mad scramble of hands and feet amongst the thrashing fish divides the booty.

Reefs are critically important to seaside residents because they maintain the shoreline, indeed entire islands, by acting as living breakwaters, constantly repairing themselves and protecting the shores from the waves. The loss of a reef community on an atoll could spell the demise of an entire island. The loss of a reef community seriously degrades the value of nearby shoreline property. Associated with many shorelines bordered by reefs are tourist industries, which depend for their livelihood on the existence of clean, wide expanses of white or pink sand beaches, and the close-by growth of corals.

Sand on coral reef beaches is a very unstable commodity, constantly being renewed and replaced. The source of the sand is the growth of coralline algae, corals and other creatures that have calcareous skeletons. Sand is generated by the many biological crunchers, drillers and digesters that with the growing parts of the reef, maintain a delicate balance between construction and destruction. A great deal of the sand they produce drifts from the ridge down the front face of the reef, but a very large part is also trapped in behind the reef top in the lagoon. The death of organisms that maintain the reef top spells the loss of the ridge and a gradual drifting of all the lagoon sand down the face of the reef. Sand drifting down eventually comes from the beach, which then begins to erode.

Many lobster tails offered in fine restaurants in Europe and North America come from coral reefs in the Caribbean and off Africa. But some delicacies are never sampled far from the sea, partly because the product is so unfamiliar that inland people would never purchase it, but also because the skill required in distinguishing poisonous from edible varieties is too great to make the product commercially useful. One example is the sea cucumber. Many species are poisonous to eat; others are delicious if prepared properly.

Biscayne Bay, off Miami, was once a deep, clear-water coral garden. Changes in drainage added so much silt that boats must now creep carefully through channels that have been dredged to allow the propellers to turn without hitting the bottom in the extremely shallow water. The famed Florida Keys, once a thriving reef system, is now in serious trouble, the result of drainage changes in the Florida everglades by the construction of canals, which has caused increased silt deposits.

The largest atoll in the world, a member of the Indian Ocean Chagos Archipelago some 150 kilometres across, has only three small islands left on it, although evidence of the former existence of many islands is to be found in the lagoons, which are filled with enormous drifts of sand. For some reason, the ecosystem of the reef was not able to keep up with the destructive effect of the waves.

All too often, seaside residents are unaware of the intimate relationship that the underwater garden has with the ground they stand on. The ocean is a convenient place to throw waste: it seems to disappear and even be used up. Up to a point, the reef can handle unexpected material, but if too much waste is thrown into the water or if there is nothing on the reef that can break it down, then it is pollution. Even changing the drainage of rivers can have a disastrous effect.

Preservation of the reef environment is a possibility. On a small scale, protective legislation closing certain reefs to exploitation by making them underwater parks, not only protects the reef, but heightens the public's awareness of this valuable resource. Informed government policies on waste dumping and unnecessary alteration of river drainages into reef areas also ensures their preservation. Because the reef is such a balanced and dynamic system, sensitive to changes in the quality of its environment, global changes in the quality of the ocean will be reflected first in the health of the reefs. Perhaps the crown-of-thorns outbreak was an early indicator of a widespread decline of ocean health.

The understanding so necessary to preserve the reefs is within our grasp. We know the reef as a dynamic, powerful ecosystem, a unique and productive part of nature. We can follow food webs, reconstruct events that produced the amazing diversity of plants and animals now living together in a delicately balanced and responsive community. We can name most reef creatures, although we do not know exactly where most of them live, what they eat, or which other creatures depend on them. But what we still cannot do is to predict the exact effect of such simple things as shell collecting. Despite this recognized inability to predict the consequences, we continue to pollute reefs, fish intensively on them and drown them in silt. Scientists need time and support for their efforts to understand the reef's complexities, and from that understanding to be able to define a reasonable use of reefs that will keep them alive forever.

Visitors to the reef must respect it, or it will disappear. Men and women, fascinated, awestruck, bring back images of grandeur, beauty and underwater majesty. The grace and immensity of manta rays moving effortlessly through the water, busy, bizarre wrasses swimming side by side with faithful butterflyfish all bespeak a world of intricate wonders. A teeming oasis in a blue watery desert, a place of intimate dependent relationships between seemingly unlikely partners, a world of merciless savagery giving no quarter for error, fragile and delicately balanced, yet serene and beautiful, the coral reef is truly magnificent.

Index